DATE DUE	
JUN 04 2012		
	AUG 06 2012	
OCT 15 2012		

知識漫畫版
（中英對照）

認識台灣歷史

A HISTORY OF TAIWAN IN COMICS

●總策劃〉吳密察　　●漫畫繪製〉劉素珍、劉昭淵　　●劇本編寫〉鄭丞鈞

●英文版策劃〉文魯彬（Robin J. Winkler）

●英文審訂〉翁佳音、賴慈芸、耿柏瑞（Brian A. Kennedy）

●英文翻譯〉何仁傑（Peter Hillman）

7　日本時代（上）：日本資本家的天堂
The Japanese Era (I): The Backyard of
Japan's Capitalists

新自然主義股份有限公司 出版

目錄

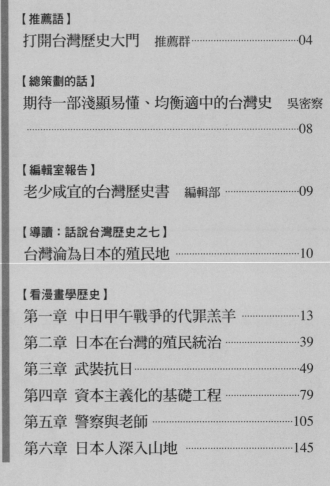

打開台灣歷史大門

小野
（知名專業作家）

台灣人越來越有信心了，
這些信心不再只是靠經濟奇蹟或政治奇蹟，
而是靠自我認同，認同自己的歷史，
認同自己的身世。
我想我會推薦這本書給我的孩子閱讀，
讓他們認同自己的身世
進而認同自己，不再自卑。

巴札克・吉靈
（台灣民主基金會主任）

當台灣逐漸民主化、多元化的今天，
我們欣喜見到人們開始願意更敞開心胸去面對
發生在這塊土地上真實的過去，
並且為未來新而完整的文化藍圖而努力。
至少這部《認識台灣歷史》讓我們看到了這樣的過程，
而且新自然主義公司洪發行人的用心及
台大歷史系吳密察老師的精研，
更令人感到佩服。

呂秀菊
（全國教師會理事長）

歷史是一個耐人尋味的故事，
也是一面鏡子。
《認識台灣歷史》從關懷出發，
走過先人的足跡，啟迪後人之智慧，
寓教於畫，格外深刻動人。

李遠哲
（中央研究院院長）

恭喜貴出版社製作完成這一套
形式與風格別具特色的台灣史書籍，
我相信在今天影像圖案與文字結合出版
特別講究的時代，這一套書對台灣的中小學生
認識自己生長的土地與社會，
必有相當大的助益。

林玉体
（台灣師範大學教育學系教授、
考試院考試委員）

《認識台灣歷史》好看又翔實，
請大家趕快來看。

城仲模
（司法院副院長）

用漫畫方式提綱挈領，
細膩分說台灣縱橫四百年史，
可謂為深入淺出，老少咸宜，
並能向上提昇作為有格調、有尊嚴的
台灣人的一部絕佳參考自修的
簡明台灣史書。

夏鑄九
（台灣大學建築與城鄉研究所教授）

這是早在我們的童年
就該看到的漫畫！

馬英九
（台北市市長）

這是一套可愛、可敬、又可讀的書。
它與八十年前連雅堂先生的《台灣通史》
雖然創作於不同的年代，採用不同的
表現方式，卻有一貫的關懷與反省。
特別的是，
這套書將趣味與嚴肅巧妙的結合在一起，
創作者及出版者的用心與努力，
都值得我們喝采。

陳水扁
（總統）

我一直認為，我們讀歷史，不僅是知道
過去做了什麼，更重要的是，我們未來要怎麼做？
然而歷史作為一種紀錄，也無可避免的受到
撰寫人本身思維或觀點的影響，而左右歷史呈現的面向。
台灣史也是如此，過去我們在求學時期，
其實並沒有完整的台灣史教學，甚至獨立的台灣史讀本，
歷史課本裡有關台灣的部分並不多，而且並非
是以台灣為主體的描述，因此大家對於台灣的歷史往往難窺全貌，
影響所及就是大家對台灣的國家定位認識不清，
今天許多爭議亦由此產生。
所以對於這套以台灣為論述主體的台灣史，
尤其是以漫畫形態表達，更是深入淺出、彌足珍貴，
對於台灣史的教育可說貢獻良多。

黃武雄
（台灣大學數學系教授）

這是一套很有啟發性的漫畫書，
大人與孩子都會喜歡看。對於大人：當作消遣，
躺在床上看了一遍，便會對台灣歷史有了整體的概念。
歷史是人類共同的記憶，台灣語族目前面臨的
兩個危機是失語病與失憶症，透過閱讀一套漫畫書，
我們能多少拾回失去的記憶。
對於孩子：看這一套漫畫，是個開始，
讓他所傳承的文化與歷史在他心中萌芽，
讓他免於記憶斷裂的挫折，
成長為一個意識健康的人。

謝長廷
（行政院院長、前高雄市市長）

《認識台灣歷史》是一個重大的突破。
它跳脫傳統歷史學者寫作方式，
用淺顯易懂的漫畫，深入淺出呈現台灣歷史的真相。
期盼藉由這套書的發行，能引起社會大眾的共鳴，
認真思考台灣永續發展的問題。

蕭新煌
（中央研究院社會學研究所研究員）

這是一本作為台灣人
不可不知的台灣史通俗漫畫版，
老少咸宜。讀台灣史，想台灣未來，
這是很好的入門漫畫集。

龔鵬程
（佛光人文社會學院文學研究所教授）

研究歷史，可以通古今之變；
了解歷史，可以幫助我們認識自己。
《認識台灣歷史》具有這兩方面的功能，
且簡明扼要，生動有趣，
非常適合社會一般人士閱讀，
新自然主義公司在
策劃、編輯、繪製、考證、撰寫的用心，
頗堪推許。

藍順德
（國立編譯館館長）

漫畫的魅力十足，
是成長過程中不可或缺的良師益友。
《認識台灣歷史》透過
生動、活潑、有趣的圖畫及故事，
可引領孩子了解自己所生長的這塊土地，
更能體會先人篳路藍縷
開拓台灣的精神。

（依姓名筆畫排列）

期待一部淺顯易懂、均衡適中的台灣史

吳密察（本書總策劃，台灣大學歷史系副教授）

　　一部深入淺出、均衡適中的歷史書，必須建立在堅實豐富的研究基礎之上，而且也必須脫離長期以來政治因素過度干涉的思想偏執。

　　這部《認識台灣歷史》試圖跳開各種成見，並充分吸收晚近的研究成果，重新勾繪台灣史的圖像。但是，當工作開始之後所遇到的困難，卻遠比預期的多。這些困難，有些是來自於必須將生硬的學院派體裁之研究成果，轉變成生動、有趣之讀物（即「戲劇化」）的過程；有些則是因為傳統歷史家大多只根據文字資料重建歷史，而且也只以文字表述歷史，但一部漫畫版台灣史則必須將歷史「視覺化」。在「戲劇化」、「視覺化」的雙重要求下，就必須要兼顧「寫實」與「示意」。這的確是一項艱鉅的工作。

　　《認識台灣歷史》雖然以淺顯的形式敘述歷史，但其中蘊含著對台灣這塊我們生活的土地及人民深厚的關愛，對台灣「如何走過來」之歷史的溫情與反省，甚至也希望對台灣的歷史教育發出改革的訊息。希望這些用心都能因讀者的耐心，點點滴滴得到共鳴。那麼，做為這部《認識台灣歷史》的企劃、監修者，將會非常高興。

老少咸宜的台灣歷史書

　　看漫畫學歷史，好看又印象深刻！《認識台灣歷史》中英對照版（十冊雙語漫畫和一冊英文版《認識台灣歷史的小百科與年表》），活潑生動、淺顯易讀，相信能帶領大家從歷史中得到樂趣，從樂趣中了解歷史。

　　這套簡明版的台灣歷史書，有編繪者的用心經營，請在翻閱時留意：

　　1. 本套書的陳述方式，以嘗試重現歷史、開放式思考為目標，力求做到：

　　　（1）中性用語，略微加入輕鬆鏡頭，增添閱讀趣味。

　　　（2）事實陳述，盡量不做價值判斷，讓讀者在史實進行中有所體會。

　　　（3）破除傳統偶像式迷思、揚善不隱惡，忠於可考證的史料。

　　　（4）對於通俗爭議，不提供標準化答案，由讀者於各種說法中自行研判。

　　2. 目前台灣的居民（Taiwanese），可以大別為「華人（Chinese）」和「原住民（Indigenous People）」。

　　　（1）「華人」包括二十世紀之前移入的福佬系、客家系，甚至二十世紀中期之後移入的「外省人」；一般常稱為「漢人（Han Chinese）」，本套書改稱「華人」。

　　　（2）一九九四年政府回應「原住民」的「正名」要求，不再稱「山胞」，本套書改稱「原住民」；這是個泛稱，其中因為語言、文化、社會組織等等的個別差異，還可以歸類成好幾族。

　　3. 本套書英文譯音均採行「通用拼音」；如有另一種說法，例如鄭成功之父鄭芝龍譯音為「Jheng Jhihlong」，但他在國外文獻上多以「Nicolas Iquan Cheng」出現，便在第二冊首次出現時，以欄外註的方式註明供參考；例外情況為台灣各縣市名、當代人名等等，則參考內政部公布的地名譯寫原則、政府年鑑、國際慣例、學術常用字等等拼注方式。

　　4. 英文版《認識台灣歷史的小百科與年表》，將十冊漫畫的精采導讀、小百科、年表、常識問答都翻成了英文，獨立成書以饗海內外讀者。

台灣淪為日本的殖民地

吳密察（本書總策劃，台灣大學歷史系副教授）

　　一八九五年，大清帝國因為甲午戰爭失敗，與日本簽訂馬關條約，將台灣割讓給了日本。甲午戰爭原本是清國與日本為爭奪對朝鮮的主導權而爆發的戰爭，而且戰爭又都在北方展開，但是結果卻割讓台灣，使得台灣的士紳們都有被朝廷遺棄的感覺。交接之後，清朝在台的巡撫唐景崧與台灣北部士紳曾試圖成立一個沒有實質內容的「台灣民主國」來抵拒日本的領有，但不旋踵而終。反而是地區性的豪強所率領的自衛武力，以簡陋的武器與日本占領軍抗戰達四個月之久。

採取強硬手段統治台灣

　　日本一反清朝時代的鬆散統治方式，積極地企圖將其支配力貫徹到台灣社會的末端，並且積極介入社會的諸多事務，於是引發原本具有自治性質的台灣地方勢力的反撲。結果，日本殖民政府以武力威壓與利益誘發併用，拉攏上層、孤立強豪的分割統治手法，花費大約十年的時間，才完成島內的綏靖工作。

　　台灣雖然是日本帝國的新領土，但日本政府卻將台灣視為殖民地，在日本帝國憲法的架構之下，另外設計一套適用於台灣的法制體系。在這套法制體系當中，台灣總督府

為台灣島內的最高行政機關，但卻沒有足以制衡它的議會。當然，台灣人也沒有參政的機會，有的只是總督府為了攏絡士紳、地方名望家族而設的名譽職或服務性質的參事、庄長等職。

一九一九年，由於同是日本殖民地的朝鮮發生主張獨立的「三一運動」，使日本政府將外地的統治政策改採「內地延長主義」。日本國內的各種政制才被施行於台灣，但仍加上各種限制。例如，台灣仍無足以牽制行政機關的議會，而是由總督府自民間挑選任命一些人組成僅供諮詢的「評議會」。

發展殖民地生產事業

日本政府在台灣達成治安的掌握之後，也對台灣的投資生產環境進行改造。最主要的是統一度量衡、統一貨幣、確立土地所有權與進行交通建設、改善都市的環境衛生。確立土地所有權是進行土地調查，一方面掌握地籍做為課徵田賦的根據，一方面則收購傳統的大租權，認定小租主為近代意義的所有權人。交通建設，最主要的是建設島內的道路系統，興築縱貫鐵路與基隆港，使西部平原生產地帶有縱橫交錯的交通網，並透過縱貫鐵路聯結北部的基隆港。於是，台灣的產品可以透過這個交通網輸往日本。

日本資本在台灣的最大投資是製糖業。殖民政府以各種優惠扶持日本資本家在台設立大型的近代製糖廠。這種製糖業，由台灣農民種植製糖原料甘蔗，提供日本資本家所

經營新式的製糖廠製糖，再將糖販運至日本國內市場。從生產到製造，再到市場的全部過程當中，日本政府都積極給予製糖產業各種政策性的配合，也因而讓製糖業成為日本在台灣最重要的殖民產業。

日本殖民政府不但積極地將其支配力滲透台灣華人的生息地帶，在一九一〇年代以後，也逐漸將行政力量伸進山區的原住民地區。早期，日本殖民政府以軍隊壓迫原住民，挺進「隘勇線」，確保淺山地區的樟腦生產地帶。接著沒收原住民槍械，試圖改變原住民的生活形態，教育原住民畜牧，甚至發展農業，使得原住民地域遭受到全面性的空前挑戰。

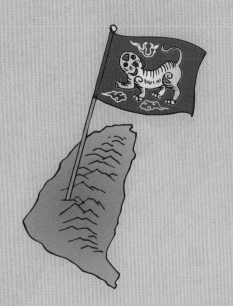

第1章
中日甲午戰爭的
代罪羔羊

A Scapegoat of
the Sino-Japanese War

一八九四年，清帝國與日本因為朝鮮問題而開戰。戰事從八月開打，清軍在戰場上節節敗退。

In 1894, a dispute over Korea between the Cing Empire and Japan led to war. The fighting began in August and Cing forces were in retreat after suffering a string of successive defeats.

在陸戰方面——
The battle scene on land ...

在海戰方面——
The battle scene at sea ...

在各國的調停之下，一八九五年三月，清帝國派全權大臣李鴻章赴日講和。

Under the mediation of various countries, in March 1895, the Cing Empire dispatched Li Hongjhang to Japan as their plenary minister for peace negotiations.

但是李鴻章到達日本後，日本卻不立刻與他談判。

Upon Li Hongzhang's arrival in Japan, however, Japan did not enter directly into negotiations with him.

李鴻章
Li Hongjhang

我們可以停戰了吧！
Can we stop the fighting now?

目前還不行。
Not yet.

為什麼不行？
Why not?

我已經來這裡談和了呀！

I am here to discuss peace!

日本首相・伊藤博文

Japanese Prime Minister, Ito Hirofumi

原來日本另有野心，想對中國做更多的勒索。

But Japan had bigger ambitions. It was planning to extract greater concessions from China.

但是，這時日本艦隊已經南下……

But at that very moment, Japanese naval forces were steaming south …

三月底，日軍已經占領澎湖。
這時日本才願意和李鴻章坐下來和談。

By the end of March, Japanese forces had occupied
Penghu Island. Only then were the Japanese willing to
sit down at the negotiating table with Li Hongjhang.

日本下關·春帆樓
Shunpanro Hotel,
Shimonoseki, Japan

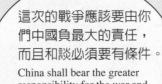

這次的戰爭應該要由你
們中國負最大的責任，
而且和談必須要有條件。

China shall bear the greater
responsibility for the war and
any peace negotiations are
conditional.

好吧，也只能這
樣子了，你們要
的條件是……

It seems we have no
alternative.What are
your demands?

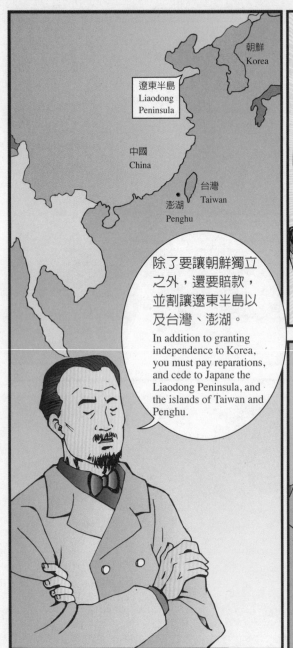

除了要讓朝鮮獨立之外，還要賠款，並割讓遼東半島以及台灣、澎湖。

In addition to granting independence to Korea, you must pay reparations, and cede to Japane the Liaodong Peninsula, and the islands of Taiwan and Penghu.

什麼，要這麼多！
What? So demanding!

對，沒錯！
I am indeed!

會議經過多次的商討，日本仍然堅持原來開出的條件。

After several more rounds of discussions, Japan held firm on its initial demands.

這一項條款能不能取消？
Isn't there any way that this condition could be removed?

不行！
No!

在日本期間，李鴻章隨時都在為條約的內容煩惱。
While in Japan, Li Hongjhang agonized day and night over the treaty' sterms.

日方的要求這麼多，該怎麼辦呢？
Japan demands so much. What shall I do?

俄國應該會干涉日本占有遼東半島,至於台灣的割讓,很可能會成為定局。

Russia may intervene to prevent a Japanese occupation of the Liaodong Peninsula. As for ceding Taiwan, it looks like nothing can be done.

這條約一旦簽下去,可說是喪權辱國了。

Signing this treaty will forfeit our sovereignty and humiliate our nation.

可是如果不答應,又不能結束這場毫無勝算的戰爭。

But if we don't sign, we can't put an end to this doomed war.

戰爭再拖下去,對中國的傷害,說不定會比割讓一個台灣還要大呢!

And if the war drags on, China may suffer even greater harm than the ceding of Taiwan.

唉,這樣比起來,還是保護中國本土重要……

From that perspective, protecting the mainland is more important.

在這樣的考量之下，李鴻章對於割讓台灣並沒有太多堅持，雙方就在四月十七日簽定「馬關條約」。

With this in mind, Li Hongjhang put up little resistance to treaty terms regarding the ceding of Taiwan and on April 17th 1895, the Treaty of Shimonoseki was signed.

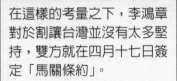

台灣便在為了保護中國本土的考量之下，成了中日甲午戰爭的代罪羔羊。

Taiwan thus became a scapegoat of the Sino-Japanese War of 1894 in the interest of protecting mainland China.

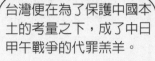

在中日簽訂的「馬關條約」中，同意將台灣、澎湖永遠讓予日本。

Under the terms of the Treaty of Shimonoseki, Taiwan and Penghu were ceded to Japan in perpetuity.

在此之前，割讓台灣的消息已外傳，朝野紛紛聯名上疏反對。確定割讓之後，台北士紳更鳴鑼罷市。

Prior to the treaty's signing, news that Taiwan would be ceded to Japan had spread. Officials and citizens circulated one petition after another voicing their opposition. Once Taiwan's fate was certain, the gentry organized a strike in protest.

註：一八九四年發生的中日「甲午戰爭」，日本稱做「日清戰爭」。
NOTE: The 1894 Sino-Japanese War is known to Japanese as the Japan-Cing War.

太可惡了，說割地就割地，完全不顧我們的死活！

It's outrageous! They summarily cede Taiwan without a thought about us!

對啊！朝廷竟連一句安慰的話都沒說，真是太無情了。

You said it! Not even a consoling word from the Emperor. It's really cold-hearted.

算了算了，乾脆我們就拜託外國人來幫忙好了。

That's it. We should just appeal for foreign assistance.

我該怎麼辦？

what am I gonna do?

台灣巡撫唐景崧
Taiwan Magistrate Tang Jingsong

朝廷就這樣把台灣割讓了，台灣的百姓也不讓我走，眼看局勢這麼混亂……

The Court is ceding Taiwan and the people won't let me leave. How am I going to get out of this mess ...

不好了！老夫人被士兵挾持了。

Bad news! Troops have taken her Ladyship captive.

不是說好，那些軍隊願意讓我高齡的老母回內地的嗎？

Didn't we already settle this? Didn't the local troops already agree to let my elderly mother return to China?

是另外一批士兵，他們懷疑老夫人可能會偷運財物出去。

It's a different group. They suspect she might try to make off with property.

我堂堂一個巡撫竟會落到這種下場，真是太悲哀了。

I have faithfully executed my duties yet still find myself in this situation. Such a disgrace.

快快，快帶我去救她。

We'll have to mount a rescue! Lead me to her at once!

是！是！

Yes Sir!

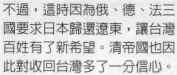

不過，這時因為俄、德、法三國要求日本歸還遼東，讓台灣百姓有了新希望。清帝國也因此對收回台灣多了一分信心。

At that very moment, however, Russia, Germany, and France were demanding that Japan return the Liaodong Peninsula to China, giving new hope to Taiwan's people and boosting the Cing Government confidence in recovering Taiwan.

大人！大人！

Sir! Your Excellency!

大人，這是剛收到的電報。

This telegram just came in, Sir.

目前局勢緊張，朝廷不方便出面，你們可以自保的名義，請各國幫忙台灣驅除日本勢力。

These are perilous times. The Court is unable to show its face but you are authorized to seek the assistance of other nations in driving out the Japanese in the name of self-defense.

有了來自清朝政府的暗示，唐景崧趕緊找門生丘逢甲來幫忙。

Taking the hint from the Cing Government, Tang Jingsong immediately sought the assistance of former student Ciou Fongjia.

丘逢甲
Ciou Fongjia

您是說，策動台灣人抗日並呼籲外國介入，以阻止日本的占領嗎？

So, we should organize the resistance among the Taiwanese and seek the help of foreign nations to prevent the Japanese occupation, is that what you're saying?

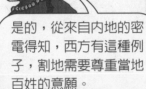

是的，從來自內地的密電得知，西方有這種例子，割地需要尊重當地百姓的意願。

Exactly! According to a secret dispatch from the Court, there truly is precedent in the West where the ceding of a territory requires the consent of the local people.

那您要我如何幫忙呢？

And how can I be of help?

希望你能運用影響力，在民間大力鼓吹成立民主國。你還可以成立義勇軍，準備抗日保鄉。

I want you to influence and motivate people to establish a democratic republic, and to organize volunteer troops to defend Taiwan against Japan.

這應該沒問題，時間緊急，我馬上去辦。

Shouldn't be a problem. But I've got to act fast. Time is of the essence!

對了，行動時要說是百姓們自己發起的，以免連累了朝廷！

Oh! I almost forgot. This is to be strictly characterized as a civic movement. You're not to breathe a word about the Court's involvement!

我辦事，您放心。

Relax. I'll take care of it.

於是，丘逢甲便向士紳們鼓吹成立民主國。

And so Ciou Fongjia agitated among the gentry for the establishment of a democratic nation.

我們成立台灣民主國，是為了向各國表明台灣百姓不願接受日本的統治！

In founding the Taiwan Republic, we seek to clearly demonstrate to foreign powers that Taiwan's people will not accept Japanese rule.

成立民主國之後，就能以台灣百姓的名義，向各國請求援助。

Once we establish a democracy, we can seek assistance from other countries on the authority of the people of Taiwan.

我們就決定在一八九五年五月二十五日這天，正式成立「台灣民主國」，並致電尋求各國的援助。

On May 25th 1895, the Taiwan Republic will be formally established and telegrams will be sent to foreign countries seeking assistance.

啪！ 啪！ 啪！

不過，清朝政府所進行的這項外交策略，並未獲得國際支持。

The Cing Government's diplomatic strategy, however, failed to win the support of the international community.

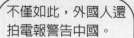
不僅如此，外國人還拍電報警告中國。
Foreign governments even sent telegrams to formally warn China.

清帝國得不到外國的支持，只好停止對台灣民主國的祕密援助，並拍電報叫唐景崧等大小官員回到中國內地。
Having failed to win foreign support, the Cing Government ended its secret support of the Taiwan Republic and sent a telegram ordering Tang Jingsong and all other officials to return to China.

太好了，朝廷終於允許我回內地了。
Smashing! The Court has finally granted me permission to return to China.

快快，快幫我收拾行李。
Get cracking! Pack my bags!

可是大人，那些軍隊可能不會放我們走。
But sir, the local troops may not let us go.

沒關係，我已經想到一招妙計了，我可以化裝成……

Not to worry. I have a plan. I will disguise myself as a …

五月二十九日，日本在台灣東北部的澳底鹽寮登陸。唐景崧與丘逢甲，以及其他大小官員，也在六月四日之後，陸續走避中國。

On 29 May, the Japanese landed in the village of Aodi in northeast Taiwan at a location they called Yanliao. Beginning on June 4, Tang Jingsong, Ciou Fongjia, and all other officials fled to China one by one.

轟！
Boom!

轟！
Boom!

唐景崧雖然改裝，不過仍被軍隊識破，遭到砲火威脅攻擊。

Although he was disguised, local troops still recognized Tang Jingsong and opened fire.

怕什麼？又沒人管我們，上面的人都已經溜走了。

What are you worried about? Nobody's in charge. Our superiors already bolted.

由於台北城局勢太混亂，有些人反而希望日本人盡快進城維持治安。

Given the chaos in Taipei, some people actually hoped the Japanese would enter the city as soon as possible to restore order.

啊！
Ah!

嚇！
Rah!

嘿！
Heh!

在此之前，受了丘逢甲的鼓吹，台灣各地已經成立大大小小的團練，這些民兵在地方領袖的領導下仍然加強操練，準備與日本抗戰到底。

Earlier, groups of volunteers, having been goaded by Ciou, had begun to gather for militia training. The civilian militia, under local leadership, continued to train in preparation to resist the Japanese.

有些準備不及的義勇，甚至把菜刀綁在竹篙上當武器。

Some of the ill-prepared volunteers were armed only with sticks with kitchen knives strapped to their ends.

喂！你拿菜刀出來幹什麼？

Hey! What's with the kitchen knife?

沒辦法，都沒有兵器了，只好拿菜刀出來湊和湊和，一樣可以殺敵！

What am I supposed to do? We've got no weapons. So we'll have to make do with kitchen knives. A kitchen knife can kill an enemy too, y'know!

當日軍南下之後，便在桃、竹、苗地區遭遇義勇軍。民兵以化整為零的方式，在林間進行游擊戰，使得日軍頭痛不已。

As the Japanese troops moved southward, Taiwan militiamen engaged them at Taoyuan, Hsinchu, and Miaoli. Breaking into small groups, the militiamen fought the Japanese using guerilla tactics.

民兵雖然奮勇抵抗，但日軍裝備精良，而且源源而來，民兵只得往南退卻。

While the militia fought bravely, the superior firepower of the Japanese, with their steady stream of reinforcements, forced them to retreat south.

原本以為能順利接收台灣的日軍，沒想到會受到這麼激烈的反抗，在兵力不足的情況下，只得趕緊請求兵力援助。

Expecting an easy occupation of Taiwan, the Japanese hadn't prepared for such intense resistance. Lacking sufficient firepower, they had to send for urgent reinforcements.

可惡！趕快發電報請求支援。

Curses! Send a telegram requesting reinforcements!

是！是！

Yes Sir!

當時駐守在南部的黑旗將軍劉永福，對北部的戰事並沒有太多支援，直到日軍推進到嘉義。

Meanwhile, General Liou Yongfu and his "Black Flag Militia" lingered in the south, lending little support to the war up north until the Japanese drew near Chiayi.

報告大人，日軍已經打來了！

Sir, the Japanese forces are upon us.

黑旗將軍劉永福
Black Flag Militia
General Liou Yongfu

是嗎？通令大家嚴加防守。

Is that so? Order all troops to be on high alert.

但是前方的黑旗軍在嘉義與日軍開戰的同時，劉永福卻已經派人求和了。

But as Black Flag troops engaged the Japanese at Chiayi, General Liou was dispatching an emissary to sue for peace with Japan.

你幫我向日軍傳達，說我不打了。

Send a message to the Japanese forces advising that we wish to end the fighting.

大人，這不太好吧！

Are you sure that's a good idea, sir?

已經沒有什麼作為了，還是趕快寫吧！

Nothing more can be done. Just do as I order.

劉永福一方面與日軍言好，一方面卻在十月十九日化裝潛逃，離開了台灣。

So Liou continued to engage the Japanese in peace negotiations while preparing for his flight on October 19 from Taiwan in disguise.

與日本抗戰四個多月之後，台灣終於被收服。許多英勇抵抗日軍的台灣人，也在這戰鬥中喪失寶貴的生命。

Taiwan was finally subdued after resisting the Japanese for more than four months. During that time, many brave souls lost their lives.

台灣民主國自主宣言

　　清帝國與日本簽訂的「馬關條約」，將台灣割讓給日本，但唐景崧與台灣士紳決定以「台灣自立」的方式，表達台灣人不願受日本統治的立場，同時希望西方國家能干涉日本占領台灣。於是在一八九五年五月二十三日發布了「台灣民主國自主宣言」，裡面寫道：

　　照得日本欺凌中國，要求割讓我國土台灣，台民曾派代表入京請願，未獲挽留。吾人聞知倭奴不日將至，吾人如屈從，則吾土吾家皆將淪為夷狄，如吾人抗拒，以實力較弱，恐難持久。屢與列強磋商，僉謂台民自先自立，然後可予援助。

　　吾台民，誓不服倭，與其事敵，寧願戰死。爰經會議決定，台灣全島自立，改建民主之國，官吏皆由民選，一切政務從公處置。但為禦敵及推行政事，必須有一元首，俾便統率，以維秩序而保安寧，巡撫兼署台灣防務唐景崧夙為人民所敬仰，故由會議公推為民主國總統。公印業已刻成，將於初二（新曆五月二十五日）巳時（上午九點至十一點）由全台紳民公呈。凡我同胞，無論士農工商，務須於是日拂曉齊集籌防局，隆重行禮。幸勿誤。

全台人民公告

大意是說：日本欺負中國，要求將台灣割讓給日本，台灣人民曾派代表到北京請願，卻無法改變割讓的事實。我們知道日本人將很快地到達台灣，我們若服從則家園將落在野蠻人手中，我們若是反抗，卻因實力較弱無法持續反抗行動。每次與西方列強討論，他們都說台灣人要先自立，才有可能幫助我們。我們台灣人決不服從日本人，寧可戰死也不要服從他們。於是，經過開會決定「台灣成立民主國」，官員從民間選出，一切政務都由眾人決定。但為了對抗敵人與處理政事，需要有一位元首，以便統治與維持秩序，因此公推台灣巡撫唐景崧為「民主國總統」，並且在五月二十五日正式成立「台灣民主國」……

　　這個「民主國」其實是徒有外表，跟我們現在說的「民主國家」不一樣，它的人民並沒有積極參與政治。另外，「民主國」的重要成員在它成立兩個禮拜後紛紛開溜，「民主國」也就跟著消失了！

第2章
日本在台灣的殖民統治
Japanese Colonial Rule on Taiwan

中國
China

台灣
Taiwan

根據一八九五年「馬關條約」，台灣及其附屬島嶼、澎湖群島永久讓予日本。

Under the terms of the 1895 Treaty of Shimonoseki, Taiwan and its constituent islands, including the Penghu Archipelago, were ceded to Japan in perpetuity.

占有了台灣，接下來該如何統治管理呢？這是日本政府面臨的新問題。

Now that Taiwan was occupied, the next matter for the Japanese Government's consideration was how to govern the place.

趁著戰勝，獅子大開口的要了這塊新領土，但到底要如何管理呢？

Like the lion, we have hungrily claimed our victory spoils, but how should they be best exploited?

伊藤博文
Count Ito Hirofumi

唉，要如何統治異民族呢？

Hmm. How should we govern a different race?

大人，雖然我們沒遇過這問題，但是可以參考外國的經驗啊！

Sir, we've never had to deal with this before, but we can refer to the experiences of other countries.

我們可以要求政府裡的外國顧問，提供他們國家統治殖民地的方法與政策來做參考。

We could ask foreign advisors to our government to provide us with information about their methods and policies for governing in their colonies.

啊！這的確是個好方法！

Ah! This is indeed a good approach.

為了吸取外國的經驗，日本人找來了兩個外國顧問，一位是英國人，一位是法國人。

The Japanese summoned two foreign advisors, one English and the other French, to learn from the colonial experiences.

我們法國對於新的國土一向採取「同化主義」。也就是說，把它們視為內地的一部分，不論法律制度或是其他規定，都和本國相同。

We French have always used the principle of "assimilation" with respect to newly colonized territories. We regard them as a part of the motherland, no matter whether in terms of the legal system or other provisions of law.

至於我們大英帝國的處理方式有很多種，我提出一種方式供你參考。

We British use many methods. I offer one for your consideration.

這種方式就是由皇帝直接統治新的殖民地。

Under this method, the emperor directly rules the newly colonized territory.

但是，在殖民地可以成立一個和母國不同的政府，並實行不同的法律制度。我們在香港和印度都是採用這種統治原則。

A colonial government can be established separate from the home country, operating under a different legal system. This is how we govern Hong Kong and India.

它們就像女王皇冠上所鑲的珠寶一樣，由女王直接擁有。

The colonies are like the jewels in the queen's crown, owned directly by the queen.

日本人經過仔細考慮之後，決定採用英國人提出的方式，把台灣當成殖民地，並且不直接適用日本法律。

After careful consideration, the Japanese decided to adopt the British way. They made Taiwan a Japanese colony in which Japanese law was not directly applicable.

根據這個法律，台灣總督可以在台灣制定具有法律效力的命令。

Under this bill, the Taiwan Governor-General may issue and implement executive orders with binding effect in Taiwan.

這樣在制定法律時，可以特別考量台灣原有的習慣，以便降低台灣百姓的反彈，也使統治可以因地制宜。

In this way, when prescribing these laws, special consideration may be given to Taiwanese customs to minimize opposition and ensure that our governance is conducted in line with local conditions.

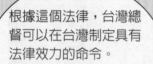

至於在台灣的日本人，則仍按照日本國的法律行事。

As regards Japanese citizens in Taiwan, they will continue to be subject to Japanese law.

也就是說，台灣人和日本人分別適用不同的法律。台灣人在法律上並不等於日本人。

In other words, Taiwanese and Japanese will be subject to different laws. Taiwanese are not equal to Japanese under the law.

啪！

等一下，我有話要說！

Hold on there! I have something to say about this!

我懷疑你們是不是真正了解近代立憲政治的精神。因為在這法律案之中，一開始就說台灣總督可以在他的管轄區域內，制定具有法律效力的命令。這是一個危險的錯誤！

I doubt you truly understand the spirit of contemporary constitutionalism. This bill states that the Taiwan Governor-General may issue executive orders with binding effect within the scope of his jurisdiction. This is a perilous mistake!

……

台灣總督是個行政官，怎麼能同時擁有立法權呢？

The Taiwan Governor-General is to be an administrative official. How can he also possess legislative authority?

這樣台灣總督就可以不受約束，按照自己行政上的方便訂定法律，完全違反立憲政治的制衡原則！

With no check on the Taiwan Governor-General, laws may be prescribed at the whim of the executive branch, contravening the checks and balances principle necessary for constitutional government.

對於這個意見，我們事前已經考慮過了。之所以決定這樣的設計，是有原因的。

Your concerns have been given consideration but we have our reasons for this decision.

因為台灣剛從中國割讓過來，整個局勢不見得會馬上穩定。

Taiwan has only just been ceded to us and conditions there will not necessarily stabilize right away.

而且台灣百姓又是不同的民族，還不清楚他們的習性。

Furthermore, the Taiwanese are ethnically different and we are as yet unfamiliar with their customs.

為了因地制宜，所以制定這些條文，讓台灣總督在行事時能有更多彈性，並且得以便宜行事。

We have enacted these provisions to give the Taiwan Governor-General more flexibility in carrying out his duties in a manner appropriate for local conditions.

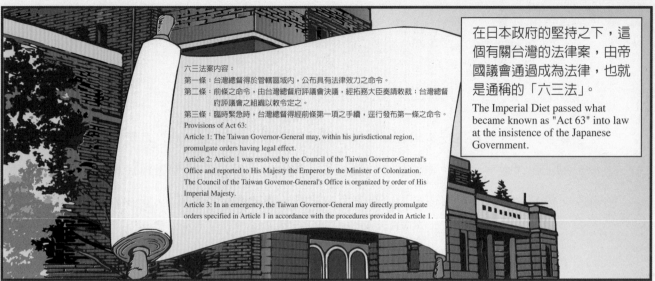

六三法案內容:

第一條:台灣總督得於管轄區域內,公布具有法律效力之命令。

第二條:前條之命令,由台灣總督府評議會決議,經拓務大臣奏請敕裁;台灣總督府評議會之組織以敕令定之。

第三條:臨時緊急時,台灣總督得經前條第一項之手續,逕行發布第一條之命令。

Provisions of Act 63:

Article 1: The Taiwan Governor-General may, within his jurisdictional region, promulgate orders having legal effect.

Article 2: Article 1 was resolved by the Council of the Taiwan Governor-General's Office and reported to His Majesty the Emperor by the Minister of Colonization. The Council of the Taiwan Governor-General's Office is organized by order of His Imperial Majesty.

Article 3: In an emergency, the Taiwan Governor-General may directly promulgate orders specified in Article 1 in accordance with the procedures provided in Article 1.

在日本政府的堅持之下,這個有關台灣的法律案,由帝國議會通過成為法律,也就是通稱的「六三法」。

The Imperial Diet passed what became known as "Act 63" into law at the insistence of the Japanese Government.

這個法律使得台灣總督在台灣除了擁有行政權,也有立法權。加上台灣總督由軍人擔任,日本天皇又賦予他軍隊指揮統帥權。

The law gave the Taiwan Governor-General both executive and legislative authority. The Governor-General was also a military officer and so authorized to command Japanese troops on behalf of the emperor.

在台灣,根本沒有人可以制衡台灣總督,台灣總督也就成了「台灣土皇帝」!

With no system of checks and balances in place, the Taiwan Governor-General was free to rule as the de facto "Emperor of Taiwan."

後藤新平

　　後藤新平十七歲進入日本須賀川醫學校就讀，一八八九年至一八九二年留學德國，關心公共衛生及社會政策，返回日本後擔任衛生局長。一八九六年曾擔任台灣總督府衛生顧問，一八九八年來台擔任台灣總督府民政局長（後改稱民政長官），到一九〇六年卸任。

　　後藤新平運用所學，擬訂治理台灣的方向，他認為制定統治政策應先了解並調查台灣社會的情況，同時用嚴酷的警察力量推行「現代化」措施。台灣的現代化都市、鐵路、電信、交通、糖業、公賣制度、警察制度、教育制度與醫療衛生等（從設立西式醫院、下水道，到動員台灣人打掃戶外環境、打掃屋內）都在他任內奠定基礎，台灣的現代化與他有相當大的關係。

　　據說後藤新平對台灣人有這樣的看法：一、台灣人怕死，要用高壓的手段威嚇；二、台灣人愛錢，可以用小錢利誘；三、台灣人重面子，可以用虛名籠絡。我們除了為殖民統治下的台灣感到悲哀之外，或許也可思考，這樣的情形是否仍存在於今日的台灣社會呢？

第3章
武裝抗日
Armed Resistance to Japan

日本參照台灣舊有習慣制定了法律，希望能夠順利統治台灣。

The Japanese hoped that prescribing laws and regulations in accordance with existing local customs would smooth its governance of Taiwan.

不過日本殖民初期，仍然受到台灣人的反抗，原因是日本人氣燄太盛，引起台灣人的不滿。

But early in the Japanese colonial period the Taiwanese, unhappy with the arrogance of the Japanese, continued to resist.

走開！走開！別擋我的路。

Back off! Get out of my way!

那麼囂張幹什麼？

What's with you?!

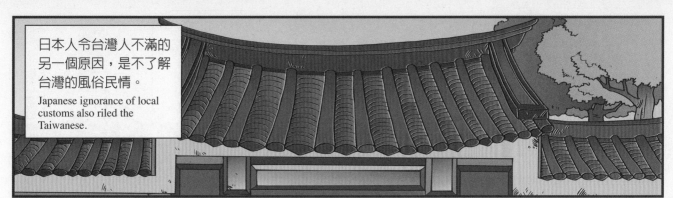

日本人令台灣人不滿的
另一個原因，是不了解
台灣的風俗民情。

Japanese ignorance of local
customs also riled the
Taiwanese.

你們不可以住
進廟裡！
You may not billet
in the temple.

為什麼不可以？
Why not?

這裡那麼寬敞，借住
一下又不會怎麼樣？
You have plenty of room.
Why can't we stay a while?

如果不肯讓我們住，
那去住你家好不好？
If you won't let us billet
here, perhaps we could all
stay at your place?!

你們會遭神明
懲罰的！
You'll incur the
wrath of the gods!

再加上當時的台灣百姓，無法適應日本引進的一些現代化制度，例如日本人要求對民家進行消毒工作。

Taiwanese at the time were also unaccustomed to some of the modernizations brought by the Japanese, for example, a program to sterilize resident's homes.

你們不要進我女兒閨房，她還沒嫁人啊！

Stay out of my daughter's room! She's not married yet.

這怎麼可以，要是房間裡不乾淨那該怎麼辦？

That's out of the question. What if her bedroom is contaminated?

啊！
Ahhh!

羞死人了！爹，你怎麼讓他們進我房裡？

How embarrassing! Father, how could you let those men into my room?

可惡的日本人，簡直一點體統都沒有。

Those blasted Japanese. They are utterly uncouth!

以往在清代，社會上的各種勢力時常
發生衝突。因為當時官府力量較小，
地方上的有力人士便會組織武力自衛
，並且出面處理地方事務。

During the Cing Era, conflicts between different
communities were common. Since the Cing
Government was ill-equipped to intervene,
local leaders emerged to handle civic affairs and
organize the armed defense of their communities.

什麼！林家的人又來
我們這裡鬧事了！

What? The Lins are stirring
up trouble again!

是的，而且他們這次
還殺傷兩個人。

I'll say! Two people were
hurt this time!

真是太可惡了。
你們馬上跟我去
討回公道！

Foul deeds indeed!
Come with me.
Let's go serve up a
little justice!

不過這些地方上的有力人士，有時也會魚肉鄉民。

But sometimes these local leaders were also local tyrants.

哈哈！沒什麼，只不過是你家的雞比別人家的肥罷了。

Ha! It happens that your hen is much plumper than everyone else's.

喂，你幹什麼搶我家母雞！

Hey, why are you stealing my hen?

真是過分。

This is outrageous.

少廢話，誰叫你繳不出保護費。

Quit your whining! You could've paid the protection fee!

咳！
Ack!

咳！
Ack!

唉，已經繳稅給官府，又要向這些人繳「土匪稅」。

Man! We already pay taxes to the government. Now we're being taxed by bandits.

對我們百姓來說，等於是「一隻牛連剝兩層皮」嘛！

For us common folk, it's like "skinning the same cow twice."

唉，又有什麼辦法呢？官府又沒能力保護我們，只能花錢消災保命了！

What else can we do? The government can't protect us, so we'll have to pay protection.

土豪有時能保護地方上的安全，但有時又像惡霸一樣。百姓對他們又愛又恨，心中充滿了無奈。

Some local warlords made their domains safer, others were merely despots. They maintained a love-hate relationship with the people, whose resentment continually seethed.

官方對於土豪，也同樣
有著又愛又恨的心情。

The warlords maintained a
similar love-hate relationship
with government officials too.

官府實際上沒有能力維持地
方的治安，必須藉助土豪的
力量，所以對他們的惡行也
只能睜一隻眼閉一隻眼。

The government lacked the power to
maintain local order so they had to
rely on the local warlords to keep the
peace while turning a blind eye to
their misdeeds.

土豪是清代社會的產
物，也就是說清代台
灣社會是由土豪自治
。這是舊式政府管理
地方的辦法。

Under Cing rule, the local
warlords had virtual
autonomy in governing their
domains, an age-old tactic of
managing local affairs.

但是日本殖民政府就不同
了，它是近代政府，連百
姓的衛生習慣都要管，何
況是那些在地方盤踞的土
豪？如此一來，雙方的衝
突是可預見的。

But the Japanese Government was
different. This was a modern
government whose influence over
its subjects extended even to
personal hygiene. How was it to
coexist with local warlords?
Needless to say, the Japanese
Government frequently found
itself at odds with the local
warlords.

土豪一旦被激怒，絕不像一般百姓好打發。為了保有既得利益，他們憑著私人武力起而對抗日本人，這就是日本人來台初期所發生的「武裝抗日」。

When provoked, the local warlords, unlike the common folk, would engage the Japanese in armed resistance to protect their interests. This was known in the early part of the Japanese Era as the "Armed Resistance to Japan."

這些土豪盤踞地方，藉著對地形熟悉的優勢，與日本人展開長期抗戰。

The local warlords were locally entrenched. With their better understanding of local terrain, they settled in for a long war of resistance against Japan.

剛開始，日本人只懂得用武力掃蕩。

Early on, the Japanese simply used armed mop up tactics.

什麼！土匪又出來騷擾，太過分了。

What? More bandits! These guys are too much!

可惡，現在全員集合，準備出發圍剿土匪，非把他們打得落花流水不可。

Blast! Assemble the men and prepare to root out the local bandits. Not one is to be left alive.

殺！
Kill them all!

殺！
Kill them all!

大人，那些是良民百姓，不是土匪。

Sir, those people are innocent folk. They are not bandits.

不管，寧可錯殺一百，也不可以錯放一人。

I don't care. "Better a hundred innocents are killed than to let not one guilty party go free."

一八九六年至一八九七年之間，總督府被台灣人的反抗搞得頭痛不已，疲於奔命。

Between 1896 and 1897, the resistance in Taiwan was an endless source of grief and consternation for the Governor-General's Office.

什麼！派出所又被襲擊了。

What? The police station was attacked again?

這些頑劣的台灣人，一定要給他們點顏色瞧瞧！

These infernal Taiwanese! We'll show them a thing or two!

再加上「寧可錯殺一百，也不可錯放一人」的錯誤政策，把許多無辜的百姓也逼成「抗日份子」。

In addition, Japan's misguided pacification policy drove many innocent ordinary folk into the arms of the resistance.

那些日本人為什麼燒光我的房子，太可惡了，那我乾脆也起來造反。

Why did the Japanese have to burn down my home? It's monstrous. I might as well join the resistance too.

討伐抗日集團的軍費不斷增加，迫使日本人不得不另外想法子。

With the military costs of wiping out the resistance steadily increasing, the Japanese were forced to rethink their approach.

經過了周密考量，日本人改採籠絡的手段。對於地方領導者，日本人投其所好，除了給予名譽職的「參事」職位，還舉辦「揚文會」、「饗老典」。

After calculation, their approach shifted to trying to win over the Taiwanese. The Japanese catered to local leaders, granting them titles such as "counselor" and even organizing poetry readings and banquets for them.

所謂「揚文會」就是台灣總督邀請文人雅士，一起寫詩唱和。

At the poetry readings, local men of letters were invited to write and recite poems with the governor.

真是無上榮耀！竟能和總督一起作詩。

It's really an incredible honor ... to be able to compose poetry with the governor. It's amazing.

對呀！以前台灣巡撫總是高高在上，連見都見不到呢！

Yea! The former magistrate lived in an ivory tower. You couldn't even get in to see him!

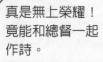

所謂「饗老典」就是指台灣總督宴請各地方的耆老一起吃飯。

At the dinner banquets, local powers were invited to dine with members of the Governor's Office.

哎喲！台灣總督竟然要請我吃飯。

Wow! The Taiwan Governor-General invited me to dinner.

真榮耀！只有像你這種有名望的人才會被邀請。

That's a real honor. Only a person of your status could receive such an invitation.

日本人想辦法迎合這些士紳，所以士紳們很容易就被收服了。

The Japanese were able to curry favor with the gentry and hence easily won them over.

哈！哈！
Ha! Ha!

哈！哈！
Ha! Ha!

對於那些頑強抵抗的土豪，日本人一方面頒布了嚴苛的「匪徒刑罰令」對付。

In the case of local warlords who stubbornly resisted, the Japanese promulgated the harsh "Criminal Punishment of Banditry Decree."

匪徒刑罰令

第一條：首魁及教唆者處死刑。

第二條：參與謀議或指揮者處死刑。

第三條：附和隨從或服雜役等處有期徒刑或重懲役。

另一方面則提供優厚的條件加以招降。

The Japanese also offered such local warlords favorable terms for surrender.

可是我們以後要靠什麼吃飯呢？

But how are we to feed ourselves in the future?

大家打游擊打了這麼久，也覺得累了吧！不如下山重新做人。

You all have been fighting a guerilla war for ages. You must be exhausted. Why not come out of the mountains and return to your normal lives?

放心，我們會幫助你們找工作的。

Don't worry. We will help you find jobs.

NOTE: Criminal Punishment of Banditry Decree:

Article 1: Leaders and instigators are punishable by death.

Article 2: Participation in planning or commanding is punishable by death.

Article 3: Those who aid or abet, etc. are punishable by prison or hard labor.

對於這些出來投降的土豪及其黨羽，總督府協助「轉業輔導」。

The Governor's Office provided "career counseling" for the now unemployed resistance fighters.

結果，有的成了在山區送信的郵差。

As a result, some became postmen in mountain areas.

有的則成了山區開路的工人。

Others became road workers in mountain areas.

這種招降政策，也讓總督府了解了土豪集團窩藏的情況。

This policy also allowed the Governor's Office to gather intelligence on the warlord organizations' hideouts.

除此之外，日本人還沿用台灣的舊制度，實行保甲法，並設立「保良局」。

In addition, the Japanese maintained the old Bao Jia system (neighborhood security system) in Taiwan and established the Bao Liang (protection of the decent citizens) Bureau.

保甲是以十戶為一甲，十甲為一保。

Under the Bao Jia system, each "Jia" consists of ten households, and each "Bao" of ten Jia.

大家都彼此相互熟悉，並規定保甲內的人負有連帶責任。

Everyone was familiar with everyone else, and every person under the Bao Jia system was responsible for each other.

警察抓到了可疑份子,會先送到「保良局」去認定,因為只有當地人才能分辨此人平時的品性和行為是否良好。

When a suspect was caught by the police, he would be transferred to the Bao Liang Bureau for identification because only local people would be able to accurately vouch for whether he was a good person or not.

嗯,這是陳家的小兒子阿土,他不是壞人。

Hey! This is Atu, a young son of the Chen family. He is not a bad guy.

如此一來,總督府在社會上便有了嚴密的監控系統,而且不致於逼良為匪,對於維持治安大有幫助。

The Governor's Office thus established a tight system of control that would not drive its subjects to banditry or rebellion.

對於這些制度，當時台灣百姓並沒有強烈反對。因為除了能獲得身家性命的保障外，也不必再應付政府之外的另一種勢力。

Among ordinary people, there was little resistance to the system. Not only were the lives and property of their families and themselves protected, they were also liberated from the predations of extra-governmental powers.

匪徒刑罰令
第一條：首魁及教唆者處死刑。
第二條：參與謀議或指揮者處死刑。
第三條：附和隨從或服雜役等處有期徒刑或重懲役。

日本殖民政府從一八九五年來到台灣，到一九〇二年將武裝土豪勢力完全鎮壓，總計處死三萬多人。

Between the arrival of the Japanese in 1895 and the final quashing of armed resistance, the Japanese Government killed more than 30,000 people in Taiwan.

從此以後，民間武裝被解除，擁有武器成為政府的專利。
Henceforth, civilians were disarmed possession of arms became the exclusive right of the government.

總督府這個近代政府取代台灣社會原本自己維持治安的工作。
The Governor's Office took over as the guarantor of public order.

The Name List of Bandits

土匪消滅以後，從一九〇二年至一九一五年間，則有另一種形式的叛亂事件。
Following the elimination of the local warlords, rebellions of a different character occurred between 1902 and 1915.

這時期大都是具有宗教結社色彩的陰謀事件，而且集中在一九一二年至一九一五年之間，這時中國正好發生辛亥革命；但這些事件並非起於台灣百姓受到中國共和革命的感召，而是……
Most were religious in nature and occurred between 1912 and 1915, on the heels of China's 1911 Revolution. However, these revolts were not directly inspired by the 1911 Revolution.

一九一三年，台灣南部——
1913, southern Taiwan

中國改朝換代了，
前朝的氣數已盡。
There's a change of
dynasties in China. The
Cing Dynasty is finished.

那台灣會有什麼改變呢？
What changes are in store for
Taiwan then?

昨天夜裡我睡覺時，三太子就來託夢。

The deity "the Third Prince" appeared to me in a dream last night.

他說有一個台灣皇帝要出來了。

He told me a Taiwan emperor would emerge.

師父，那會是什麼樣的人？

Master, what will he look like?

我不是有帝王相嗎？

Don't you think I have the look of an emperor?

……

走！全部帶走！
Move! Take them all away!

這類陰謀叛亂事件大概有十次之多，有時捉到三、四個人，有時捉到十多人，其中比較有組織的事件，是一九一五年的「西來庵事件」。

There were about ten of these incidents. In some, just three or four people were arrested while in others up to dozens were arrested. Some were more organized. One such incident was the Silai Temple Incident of 1915.

這次事件的首領余清芳等人，利用西來庵聯繫黨員。

The leader of this movement, Yu Cingfang, communicated with followers through the Silai Temple.

余清芳
Yu Cingfang

他們爭取的對象都是農民、勞動者，並以宗教進行宣傳。

They promoted their cause through religion, focusing on farmers and laborers.

西來庵事件不僅規模最大,而且被日本懲處的人數也最多。

The Silai Temple Incident was the largest movement of its kind in Taiwan with the largest number of people sentenced by the Japanese as a result.

在這個事件之後,台灣的武裝抗日事件就落幕了。

This was the last armed resistance movement against Japan.

至於這些陰謀叛亂份子,總督府都交由司法審判,不像對付土豪時,只要一捉到就任意處置了。

The Governor's Office handed the conspirators over to the judiciary for trial. They were not summarily executed as the local warlords had been.

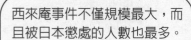

別跑!
Stop!
Freeze!

日本殖民政府設置臨時法院審理這些案子,在程序上還算講究。

The Japanese established a provisional court to hear the conspirators' cases and the procedure proved quite practical.

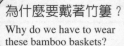

為什麼要戴著竹簍?
Why do we have to wear these bamboo baskets?

日本殖民政府透過司法審判的方式，讓台灣善良百姓覺得將這些人判刑是替社會除掉敗類，自然不易產生抗拒的心理。

Law-abiding Taiwanese saw the Colonial Government's convictions of criminals as helping rid society of undesirables through the judicial process. Ordinary Taiwanese had no natural impulse to resist.

你們現在只是嫌疑犯，戴上竹簍是為了不要讓別人看清你們的臉，這是保障你們的人權。

You're all merely suspects. The baskets will conceal your identity. They're to protect your rights.

什麼嫌疑犯，你們只會做做樣子而已，最後還不是判死刑！

What do you mean "suspects?" That's just for show. We all know that the sentence will still be death!

廢話少說，趕快戴上。

Cut the nonsense and put the basket back on!

到了一九一五年，所謂的宗教結社事件也被日本人肅清了。

By 1915, Japan had successfully put down these religiously inspired uprisings.

日本人花了二十年的時間，把社會裡的兩大問題，也就是土匪與宗教叛亂事件，完全解決。

It had taken 20 years for Japan to fully solve its two major problems in Taiwan: local warlords and religiously inspired uprisings.

從此以後，日本人可算是牢牢的控制住台灣了。

Henceforth, Japan was in firm control of Taiwan.

吳鳳神話

　　以前，所有的國小學生都讀過一則吳鳳的故事。

　　很久以前（清代）有一位在鄒族地區擔任通事的人，名叫吳鳳。因為他常為鄒族人調解與華人的糾紛，贏得鄒族人的愛戴。他並要求鄒族人不再出草獵人頭做祭神的供品，改以豬頭代替，鄒族人聽了他的話。不料不久之後發生乾旱糧荒，鄒族人以為是老天懲罰，苦求吳鳳准許再獵人頭。吳鳳於是決定要「捨身取義」，便答應鄒族人可以在某時某地射殺一名紅衣人。鄒族人依約前往，射殺這位紅衣人，結果發現他竟是吳鳳！傷心的族人紛紛跳崖自殺……

　　這一篇教大家要學習吳鳳寬厚、仁慈、博愛的教材，卻曾傷害許多原住民的小朋友。許多鄒族人表示吳鳳原來是個壓榨原住民的通事，才會被殺；而日本殖民政府為了開發阿里山森林資源，將吳鳳的事蹟加以美化渲染，編造出上述的吳鳳神話，做為他們的政策宣傳；後來國民黨政府也繼續使用這個吳鳳神話，將吳鳳說成是教化原住民達到文明的義人，以傳揚「儒家精神」及國民犧牲奉獻的精神。

　　如今教科書中刪除了這個「吳鳳神話」，原本樹立在嘉義市圓環的吳鳳像被拉倒移開，嘉義縣的吳鳳鄉也改名叫阿里山鄉了。

第**4**章
資本主義化的基礎工程

Laying the Foundations
of Capitalism

為了糾正舊有惡習，日本人規定隨地便溺要罰錢。

To rectify bad habits, the Japanese began fining people for relieving themselves in public.

天啊！現在連大小便都要罰錢！

Good heavens! Now there's even a fine for relieving oneself!

為了改善衛生條件，日本殖民政府制定許多新規定。

The Colonial Government introduced numerous new rules to improve sanitary conditions.

在一八九五年，立即蓋了一間比較像樣的現代醫院「台北醫院」，也就是現在台大醫院的前身。

In 1895, Taipei Hospital, a relatively modern hospital and the predecessor to Taiwan National University Hospital, was built.

日本殖民政府積極改善台灣的衛生條件，也加裝了新式的自來水設施，因為如果不這麼做，就沒有日本人願意來台灣了。

The Colonid Government aggressively improved sanitation conditions in Taiwan and also installed a modern piped-in running water system. Without these improvements, no Japanese would be willing to come to Taiwan.

真是臭死了！

This place really smells!

把衛生條件改善之後，緊接著要做的是基礎交通建設。

After sanitation conditions were improved, the next item on the agenda was basic transportation infrastructure.

為了能讓南北貨物流通，日本殖民政府又修築了南北縱貫鐵路。

To facilitate the smooth shipment of goods between north and south, the Japanese refurbished the north-south railway line.

你看看，劉銘傳以前鋪的這條舊鐵路，鋪得真糟糕！

Check it out! The old railway line Liou Mingchuan built. What a mess!

對啊，火車走在這種鐵路上，爬坡時恐怕都跑不過我，難怪現在要重鋪。

Yeah! Even I can outrun these trains when they're running uphill. No wonder it's being rebuild.

哈！哈！哈！
Ha! Ha! Ha!

註：三義舊稱三叉河；高雄舊稱打狗。
NOTE: Sanyi was called Sanchahe and Kaohsiung was called Takau.

縱貫鐵路完成之後，南北的貨物更容易流通。

After the north-south line was completed, goods could be more easily transported between north and south.

這麼多的砂糖要運到哪裡？

Where could so much sugar be headed?

你一定是新來的，對不對？

You must be new, right?

對！對！

Yes! Yes!

日本
Japan

台灣
Taiwan

這些砂糖由火車載到基隆港，再由輪船運到日本，了解了嗎？

The sugar is hauled by train to Keelung Harbor, and then shipped by freighter to Japan. Got it?

了解了，謝謝你。

Yes. Thank you.

縱貫鐵路除了對經濟有很大的幫助，也使得人與人更容易交流，視野更廣闊，同時造成全台灣人認同觀念的形成，這是當初日本人所料想不到的。

The railway system not only benefited the economy, but also enabled people to interact more frequently, which in turn broadened their horizons and helped them form an identity. It was a development the Japanese had not expected.

基隆港
Keelung Harbor

當時台灣的港口設施不好,許多大型船隻都無法停泊。

At the time, Taiwan's harbor facilities were poor and many large ships were unable to moor there.

看到港口了,終於可以上岸了。

I can see the harbor now. At last I can go ashore.

船速減慢了?咦!怎麼停了下來?

Huh? Why are we slowing down? Why are we stopping?

喂喂喂,為什麼船停了下來?是不是發生什麼問題?

Hey! Why have we stopped? Is there something wrong?

第二天早上
The next morning

對不起，您昨天不是說天亮之後就能進港，為什麼船到現在都還沒開動？

Excuse me, sir. Didn't you say yesterday that the ship could enter the harbor at daybreak? Why aren't we moving yet?

船不會再前進了。
The ship won't be moving any closer.

啊？
為什麼？
Huh? Why?

那我們要怎麼上岸？
Then how do we disembark?

現在正在等小船來載我們。
We must wait for a skiff to take us ashore.

沒有好的港口，除了增加往來的困難外，也沒辦法把台灣的物資運出去。

Without good harbors, the difficulties of contact between Taiwan and the outside world were compounded, and goods from Taiwan could not be exported.

日本人來台灣之初，便把興築基隆港列為首要工作，一八九九年至一九○二年完成第一期工程。一九○八年完成第二期工程。

In the initial stages of the Japanese arrival in Taiwan, they made the rebuilding of Keelung Harbor a priority. Between 1899 and 1902, the first stage of work was completed. In 1908, the second stage of work was completed.

基隆港
Keelung
Harbor

靠著這些港口，台灣的物資才得以源源不斷的大量出口。

These harbors made it possible for large quantities of Taiwan goods to be easily exported overseas.

高雄港
Kaohsiung Harbor

至於高雄港，也於一九○八年至一九一二年間完成第一期的工程。

The first stage of work on Kaohsiung Harbor was completed between 1908 and 1912.

日本人還在台灣修築了上萬公里的公路。

The Japanese also built more than 10,000 kilometers of roads in Taiwan.

交通建設做好之後，貨物的往來就非常方便，不過想使貨物更容易買賣，就要有統一的交易媒介，也就是統一的貨幣和度量衡。

After the transportation infrastructure was completed, the movement of goods became very convenient. However, to facilitate trading of goods, a unified transaction media – a single currency and a single system of measure units – was needed.

清代幣制非常混亂，有銅錢，也有銀幣，還有民間私鑄的錢。

The currency system during the Cing Era was disordered. There were copper coins and silver coins, and some privately minted currencies.

這種幣制混亂的情形，會妨礙經濟的發展。於是日本人便在一九一一年，將台灣的幣制統一。

This situation was an impediment to economic development. So Japan unified Taiwan's currencies in 1911.

日本人還把台灣的度量衡統一。

Japan even standardized the systems of weights and measures used in Taiwan.

台灣原來所使用的度量衡不僅種類繁多，而且製作與修理都任由民間隨意處理。

Scales originally used in Taiwan were not only wildly varied in type, but were also made and maintained by their users as they saw fit.

日本統治台灣以後，總督府就開始著手改革。

After assuming control of Taiwan, the Governor's Office began reforms.

一九〇〇年開始改用日本式的度量衡，後來更漸漸禁止使用舊式度量衡了。

Beginning in 1900, Japanese standard weights and measures were adopted and use of the old scales was gradually prohibited.

日本人也在台灣進行土地調查，確定土地所有權。

The Japanese also commenced land surveys in Taiwan to confirm land ownership.

所有權確定之後，除了讓政府增加稅收外，土地買賣也有了保障。透過這次土地調查，日本殖民政府也將很多無主土地收歸政府所有。

By confirming ownership, the government increased tax revenues and land transactions were guaranteed. Land surveys also allowed the Colonial Government to take possession of many parcels of unclaimed land.

由於台灣位居亞熱帶，氣候上非常適合種植甘蔗，所以日本殖民政府鼓勵台灣人種植甘蔗。

Taiwan's subtropical climate favored the cultivation of sugarcane, so the Colonial Government encouraged the Taiwanese to cultivate sugarcane.

但是日本國內缺糖，每年需要從國外進口很多糖，無形中造成外匯流失，也就是讓日本國內的錢流到國外了。

Japan lacked sugar domestically and had to import large quantities each year. This gave Japan a negative balance of trade each year. In other words, money from Japan was flowing overseas.

所以日本人便想在台灣種甘蔗來製糖，以供應國內所需。

So the Japanese wanted to cultivate sugarcane in Taiwan to supply domestic demand in Japan.

這一項政策果然大大成功，最後台灣成了蔗糖王國。

The policy was successful and Taiwan eventually became a cane sugar powerhouse.

日本殖民政府打算將台灣改造成為蔗糖王國，不過在這之前必須做一些吸引日本資本家來台投資的措施。

The Colonial Government planned to make Taiwan into a cane sugar powerhouse. However, before it could do so, some measures were needed to encourage investment in Taiwan by Japanese capitalists.

台灣傳統的糖廍不僅規模較小，而且設備簡陋，生產的糖品質不好，量又少。

Taiwan's traditional cane sugar refineries were small and their equipment crude. So the sugar they produced was of poor quality and limited volume.

這種生產量，不僅無法供應日本國內的需要，而且還賺不了錢。

This level of production volume is not only insufficient to supply Japanese demand, but will also fail to turn a profit.

所以必須成立近代的大型糖廠。

Therefore modern large cane sugar refineries must be established.

可是要叫誰來做呢？
But who can be called upon to do this?

很簡單。
No problem.

難道你有好辦法？
Do you have a good plan?

我們可以讓國內的大資本家來投資。
Just let Japanese capitalists make the investments.

這個主意不錯，不過那些資本家願意來嗎？
It's not a bad idea. But will they be willing to come over?

另外，新式糖廠成立之後，還要想辦法確保我們的蔗糖市場。

We also need to protect market share for the large quantity of sugar that will be produced by our new style sugar refineries.

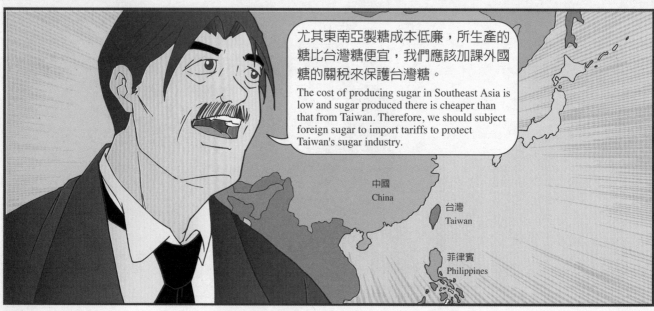

尤其東南亞製糖成本低廉，所生產的糖比台灣糖便宜，我們應該加課外國糖的關稅來保護台灣糖。

The cost of producing sugar in Southeast Asia is low and sugar produced there is cheaper than that from Taiwan. Therefore, we should subject foreign sugar to import tariffs to protect Taiwan's sugar industry.

中國
China

台灣
Taiwan

菲律賓
Philippines

於是，台灣新式糖廠一間
間蓋起來，砂糖一包包的
載往日本。

So modern sugar refineries were
built one after another in Taiwan,
and the final product began to flow
continuously into Japan.

在台灣投資製糖廠的日本
資本家，紛紛賺了大錢。

The Japanese capitalists who
invested in sugar refineries in
Taiwan all made fortunes.

大糖廠需要大量的製糖甘蔗，台灣農民所種的甘蔗能賣出去，蔗農也就有錢可賺。

Large sugar refineries need large quantities of raw materials. With a ready market for their sugarcane, Taiwan's farmers made good money too.

台灣農民
Taiwan farmer

日本資本家
Japanese sugar capitalists

不過，和那些日本資本家比起來，蔗農畢竟還是被剝削的一群，所以後來便有人領導他們起來抗爭。

Compared to the Japanese sugar capitalists, however, the Taiwanese farmers were inevitably exploited. They later organized a protest.

這種由台灣農民種植，再由日本資本家掌管加工製造的製糖業，便成為日本時代最重要的殖民地產業。

The sugar refining industry, built and operated by the Japanese capitalists, was the most important of Japan's colonial industries.

台灣的製糖產業

日本時代，台灣最大的殖民產業就是糖業。二十世紀初，台灣總督府獎勵新式糖廠，並把日本資金大量引入台灣，徹底打垮了台灣本地傳統糖廍。

一九〇一年開始陸陸續續有多家日本人的「製糖會社」（製糖公司）成立。日本政府以警察誘導台灣人低價出售耕地，並釋出官有地扶植日本製糖資本家，還規定蔗農必須把生產的原料賣給指定的製糖會社，但價格卻由會社單方面決定。

由於製糖會社還會偷斤減兩，例如有甘蔗送到廠內秤重，會社為了剝削蔗農，竟會在磅稱上動手腳，然而其實蔗農憑著多年來的經驗，對於送去過磅的甘蔗重量多少大概心裡有數，果然過磅後與蔗農預估差了一大截，讓蔗農心中暗暗叫苦。

當時蔗農雖然有一定的利潤，但是將所得拿去還清事前向會社借來買苗、買肥料的錢及利息，以及付給地主的租金，剩下來便沒有多少錢了。難怪當時有人說「第一憨，選舉運動；第二憨，種甘蔗給會社磅」。

日本時代，日本資本家所經營的糖業的「成就」，便是這樣建立在台灣蔗農的苦難及血淚之上。

第 **5** 章
警察與教師
The Police and Educators

清代地方上的事務大體上是自治的，所以才會出現土豪控制的情形。日本殖民政府卻不再假手他人，為了掌控社會，它以「街庄役場」、「警察、派出所」、「學校」這三者配合，將控制力滲透到地方。

Local affairs during the Cing Era were handled mostly autonomously, which in part led to the emergence of local war lords. However, the Japanese Colonial Government decided to handle matters directly. It used local government offices, police stations, and schools to extend its control of Taiwan society.

街庄役場就是現在的鄉鎮公所，是地方的行政機關，主要進行政策的告知與宣傳。

Local government offices were like the township offices in Taiwan today. They were the local administrative bodies and they were primarily engaged in the notification and propagation of policies.

街庄役場

總督府為了維持治安，並徹底實行各種政策，讓警察擁有很大的權力，甚至人民的衣食住行都能管。由於他們在執勤上非常嚴苛，台灣人對警察是又恨又怕。

The Governor's Office had empowered the police with great authority to maintain order and fully implement its policies, even extending to what people wore, what they ate, where they lived and where they went. As the police strictly enforced their duties, the Taiwanese came to hate and fear them.

日本警察不但是各種政策的執行者，也是社會的監督者。

The Japanese police were not only the enforcement agents of various policies, but also societal monitors.

不管任何事，只要警察覺得人民有錯，就會給予嚴厲的懲罰。

Regardless of the infraction, if the police felt someone was in the wrong, harsh punishment could be exacted.

喂！你在這裡幹什麼？

Hey! What are you doing there?

你還跑！

You dare run!

快逃！

I better boogie!

還敢逃！混蛋，竟然這麼不衛生！

Moron! How dare you run away! You're so grubby!

對台灣人來說，警察就是日本殖民政府的代表，不僅非常嚴厲，甚至仗勢欺人或故意刁難。所以很多台灣文學作品裡，常常看到對警察醜陋面的描述。

To the Taiwanese, the police were the Colonial Government's representative and were harsh to the point of bullying, intentionally making life difficult for people. Works of Taiwanese literature are rife with descriptions of the ugly side of the police.

例如日本時代台灣文學家賴和，在〈一桿稱仔〉短篇小說中，就很生動的把日本警察刁難民眾的情形寫了出來。

For example, in his book, *A Steelyard*, colonial-era Taiwanese writer Lai He portrayed vivid accounts of Taiwanese people suffering at the hands of the Japanese police.

一桿稱仔

賴和◎著

台灣人大多老實勤奮，為了家計努力打拚。話說一位窮苦的百姓阿得在街上賣菜，賣了一天，好不容易賺了一點錢。

The Taiwanese were mostly honest and industrious people who worked hard to provide for their families. In one story, a poor greengrocer named A-de was selling vegetables on the street. He was lucky to make a small amount of money after a whole day's work.

這時一個日本警察走了過來。

Suddenly, a Japanese policeman approached him.

你賣的花椰菜看起來不錯，賣多少錢？

These cauliflower shoots look good. How much are they?

是的！是的！

Yes! Yes!

大人需要的話，不用問價錢，您肯要我的東西，是我運氣好。

Sir, you need not to ask the price. If you would take them, I would be very happy to give them to you.

不不，你先給我稱稱看。

No. No. Weigh them first.

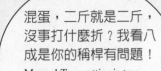

由上面的故事可以看到，當時警察執勤不僅嚴格，有時甚至吹毛求疵。

You can tell from that story that the police were often harsh and sometimes even spiteful for no reason.

不過，由於執行嚴格，確實使得許多新制度很快的建立起來。

The severity of enforcement, however, definitely permitted the rapid establishment of many new institutions in Taiwan.

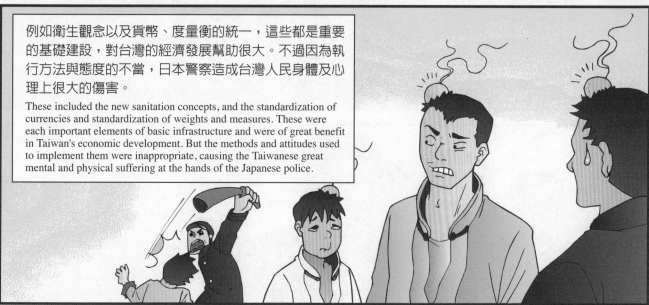

例如衛生觀念以及貨幣、度量衡的統一，這些都是重要的基礎建設，對台灣的經濟發展幫助很大。不過因為執行方法與態度的不當，日本警察造成台灣人民身體及心理上很大的傷害。

These included the new sanitation concepts, and the standardization of currencies and standardization of weights and measures. These were each important elements of basic infrastructure and were of great benefit in Taiwan's economic development. But the methods and attitudes used to implement them were inappropriate, causing the Taiwanese great mental and physical suffering at the hands of the Japanese police.

警察還負責很多不同性質的任務。例如製糖公司從國外引進新品種的甘蔗，也由警察向農民推廣。

The police were also responsible for a disparate range of tasks. For example, when a sugar company imported a new breed of sugarcane, the police would be in charge of promoting it.

各位注意，這是從國外引進的甘蔗新品種，你們可以種種看。

Listen up! This is a new breed of sugarcane imported from overseas. Give it a try in your fields.

種了會有什麼好處？

What are the benefits?

這種甘蔗非常容易照顧，又可以榨出更多的糖分。

This breed of sugarcane is very easy to care for, and more cane sugar can be extracted from it.

這麼好啊！那我就來試試看。

That sounds great! I'll give it a try.

一般百姓的生活習慣也由警察來指導。

The police also directed the daily living habits of the common folk.

喂！下星期一要進行大掃除。

Hey! Next week you need to get started with the cleanup.

什麼大掃除？

What cleanup?

是居家環境的大掃除。

The cleanup of residential living spaces.

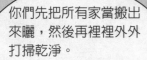

你們先把所有家當搬出來曬，然後再裡裡外外打掃乾淨。

Start by moving all furniture outside to dry in the sun, then clean everywhere both inside and outside the house.

這樣會不會太麻煩？

Isn't that too troublesome?

這樣才能有個衛生乾淨的居家環境，麻煩一點又有什麼關係。

This is the only way to have a clean living environment. It's never too troublesome.

可是要把所有家當全搬出來，實在太……

But moving all furniture outside is really too …

這是規定，不得違抗！

You have no choice. It's a rule!

幾個鐘頭之後——
A few hours later.

終於可以回復原狀了。
At last things can go back to normal.

喂！你等一下。
Hey! Wait a second.

怎麼了？
What is it?

在台灣的日本警察因為被賦與很大的權力,有時還可以執行法官才有的審判權,而且日本時代前期還有笞刑,可以打人。

The Japanese police were given great authority in Taiwan and were sometimes empowered to exercise authority normally reserved for judges. In the early days of the Japanese Era, they could even administer corporal punishment.

你逃不了!
You won't escape!

終於被我抓到了,你為什麼偷東西?
I finally got you! Why do you steal?

偷東西就是不對,講都講不聽!今天非得好好教訓你一頓不可。
It's wrong to steal! You never learn! This time I'll teach you a proper lesson.

還要被關啊？
I have to go to jail too?

對啊！誰叫你要偷東西。
That's right! No one asked you to steal!

不但要關你，我還要叫你繳罰款哩！
You'll not only go to jail, but also pay a fine!

大人，你就行行好，不要關我了。
Sir, please be lenient. Don't send me to jail.

帶走！
Take him away!

是！
Yes Sir!

台灣的警察一直都是由日本人擔任，一直到統治後期，才有台灣人擔任較低階的警察。只要台灣人犯了一點小錯誤，日本警察馬上就變成了凶神惡煞。

Taiwan's police were exclusively Japanese until the latter part of the Japanese Era when Taiwanese were finally permitted to serve in lower positions. When a Taiwanese committed even the slightest infraction, the Japanese police would be ready to pounce.

警察是日本時代台灣人心中永遠的陰影，有時連小孩子都能感受到這種恐怖的壓力。

The Japanese police cast an ever-present shadow over the Taiwanese, a fear shared even by the children.

在日本時代，警察代表「統治的威力」，教育系統下的老師則代表「文明的溫情」。日本殖民政府為了讓台灣人了解政令，也鼓勵台灣人上學，接受日本教育。

During the Japanese Era, the police represented "the power of governance," while the teachers represented "the warmth of civilization." The Colonial Government strongly encouraged Taiwanese to attend schools in order to better understand government regulations.

不過，初期台灣百姓並不是非常支持日本人所辦的新式學校，因為這種學校制度與清代的完全不同。

However, early in the Japanese Era, the Taiwanese weren't particularly supportive of the new style schools organized by the Japanese, which were completely different from those of the Cing Era.

在清代——
During the Cing Era

孩子，你要好好用功讀書。我們陳家歷代都種田，沒有人讀過書，不過你的資質不錯，是個可造就的人。

Study hard my son. The Chen family have been farmers for many generations. None of us has ever gone to school. But you have what it takes to succeed.

我賣了田，花錢請先生到家中來教你，你可不要辜負家裡對你的期望啊！

I've sold some fields to afford a tutor for you. Don't let us down!

爹，我知道。
Yes father.

知道就好，希望明年你到縣裡參加科考，能考個生員回來，讓我們陳家光耀門楣。

Good. I hope you make the Chen family proud next year by passing the county's first civil examination.

在傳統的觀念裡，讀書就是為了參加科舉、光耀門楣；如果考不上，至少也能學會寫信和記帳。

Traditionally, the purpose of study was to sit for the civil examinations and bringing honor upon one's family. Even if one didn't pass, one would still learn writing and bookkeeping skills.

雖然中國歷代都設有學校,不過那只是為配合科舉制度而設的,而且必須通過縣試,成為「童生」,才能入學就讀。這種學校,就好像輔導學生參加考試的補習班,目的只為了考上科舉,跟我們後來的學校不同。

Although the previous Chinese dynasties had all established schools, the "schools" were actually a part of the examination system. To attend a school, a kid would first have to pass a test at the county level to become a "candidate." These "schools" – similar to today's cram schools – helped students prepare for the next examinations.

但是日本時代的學校就不同了,除了教授日語及生活上的知識,同時也是宣傳政令、灌輸國家意識的機關。

However, schools during the Japanese Era were different. In addition to teaching the Japanese language and knowledge about daily living, they also provided information about government rules, and indoctrinated the people with nationalist ideology.

早期，台灣人並不是很想上日本殖民政府的新式學校。

Initially, the Taiwanese were not interested in sending their children to the new Japanese schools.

希望你能將小孩送到學校上課。

I hope you will send your child to school.

我看不用了，現在讀書又不能考試做大官，還讀它做什麼？

No need to. Nowadays, going to school does not guarantee you a position as a high official through the imperial civil examination system. So what's the point of it?

更何況小孩去讀書，家裡少了幫忙的人手，這實在划不來，不讀了！

Besides, if our child attends school, then our family has one less helping hand. It just not worths it. I'm not sending him.

日本老師只好到家裡去遊說。

So the Japanese teachers would visit the kids' homes and plead with their parents to let them go to school.

你應該讓小孩到學校讀書。

You should let your children go to school.

老師您實在太熱心了，但我的小孩實在不適合讀書。

You're very kind. But my children are not really cut out to be students.

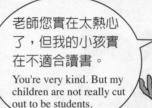

每個人都應該讀書，讀書對小孩有很大的幫助。

Every person should go to school. Going to school will truly benefit your children.

唉呀！您太客氣，既然老師都來到家裡了，那我也不好意思拒絕。

You're really kind. And since you've come all the way to our home, I guess I can't refuse.

到一九一〇年之後，日本的統治已經漸漸穩固，台灣人才開始比較積極的送小孩去讀「番子冊」。

By 1910, Japan had consolidated its control of Taiwan and the Taiwanese had actively begun to send their children to study the "barbarian books."

莎喲娜啦
（再見）！
Sayonara
(Good-bye)!

日本人只著重辦初級的學校，他們並不想讓台灣人學得更高深的學問，因為他們認為書讀得越多的人就越難管。

The Japanese focused on primary schools only. They did not want the Taiwanese to attain higher education since intellectuals were harder to govern.

台灣人與日本人讀的學校也不相同。台灣人讀的小學稱為「公學校」，日本人讀的稱為「小學校」。「小學校」的師資與程度比「公學校」好很多。

The Taiwanese and Japanese were also different in terms of the content of their education.
The primary schools for the Taiwanese children were called "public schools," while those for the Japanese children were called "elementary schools" and boasted far better faculty and curricula.

到了一九二〇年，這種不公平的待遇才有了些微的改變。

By 1920, there was a minor change with respect to this unfair treatment.

所謂的改變，是在「小學校」每一個班級裡開放幾個名額，讓台灣人就讀。

That change permitted a few Taiwanese children to join each class at the Japanese elementary schools.

當時學校教育採類似軍事化的方式管理。學生們被要求穿著整齊的制服，背著書包到設有圍牆的學校上課。

Schools of the day were administered with a military mindset. Students were required to dress neatly, wear uniforms and carry the same school bags.
The schools were surrounded by walls.

進入學校之後，小學生所要學習的課程有「國語」，就是日本語；「修身」則是類似現在的「生活與倫理」；以及「算術」、「歷史」、「地理」、「理科」等科目。

Once at school, students studied the "national language" (Japanese), ethics, math, history, geography, and science.

老師除了按照固定的教科書教學外，還會在課堂上灌輸日本天皇的尊貴，以及日本國的偉大、日本的歷史。另外，在鄉下的學校還有農業實習課程。

In addition to the required textbooks, instruction also included respect for the Japanese emperor, the greatness of Japan and Japan's history. In the countryside, practical training courses in agriculture were also offered.

到了教室，學生們要聽鈴聲作息。這種管理方式就好像把學校當成軍營一樣，強調秩序、紀律。

Once in class, the bell signaled work and rest for the students. This administrative style essentially turned the schools into military camps emphasizing order and discipline.

噹！噹！

噹！

噹！噹！

噹！

這種以「訓練」為主的教育，還一直持續到現在。

This educational emphasis on training continues to this day.

現在很多老人家回想起日本時代，印象最深刻的就是日本老師及日本警察。

Today, when the elderly recall the Japanese Era, teachers and policemen are often their most lasting memories.

老師和警察這兩種人與
台灣人的生活密切相關
，而且分別代表了好日
本人與壞日本人。

Policemen and teachers were
an integral part of Taiwanese
life. The teachers represented
the good Japanese while the
policemen represented the bad
ones.

因為日本老師對小朋友非常
關心，在今天有些老人家，
還以感恩的心情邀請老師從
日本來台灣參加同學會。

The great care Japanese teachers
showed for their Taiwanese pupils
sometimes prompts elderly
Taiwanese to invite their former
teachers to Taiwan for class reunions
to show their gratitude.

同學會
Class Reunion

這是大家一起出
錢打造的金牌，
送給老師。

This golden plaque is
a gift from all of us.

哎呀，這怎麼
好意思。
You shouldn't have.

老師，沒關係，就收下吧！

It's nothing, really, teacher!

這……這怎麼好意思？

Oh ... How can I possibly accept?

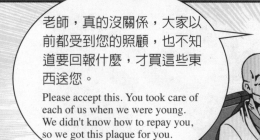

老師，真的沒關係，大家以前都受到您的照顧，也不知道要回報什麼，才買這些東西送您。

Please accept this. You took care of each of us when we were young. We didn't know how to repay you, so we got this plaque for you.

太感謝了！
太感謝了！

Thank you so much!

日本人利用警察威嚇、老師教化的方式，把台灣社會控制得牢牢的，百姓們也都能規規矩矩的過日子。

The Japanese used the intimidation of the police and the education provided by the teachers to bring Taiwan society under control. From then on, the Taiwanese went through their lives in orderly fashion.

日本時代的台灣教育

　　日本時代為台灣近代的西式教育奠定基礎，然而建立這個制度的主要目的卻是在幫助日本殖民統治。

　　我們可分三個時期來看日本時代的教育：第一個時期是一八九五年到一九一九年，總督府在領台之後很快的設立以日語教學為主的「國語傳習所」及六年的「公學校」（原住民就讀「番人公學校」），台灣人能夠就讀的中等以上學校只有國語學校（培養初等教育師資）、醫學校、糖業及工業講習所等等。這個時間並沒有明確的教育政策，但卻已分為台灣人、原住民、日本人三個差別待遇的教育系統。

　　第二個時期自一九一九年到一九三○年代初期，因為一九一八年第一次世界大戰後，世界各國「民族自決」與要求民主的風潮興起，迫使總督府必須改變對殖民地的統治方式。一九一九年頒布了「台灣教育令」，初等教育有公學校，中等以上則設實業（農、工、商）學校、高等普通學校、師範學校、農林及商業專校及醫專。

　　高等學校的設置幾乎都有特殊目的，例如醫學校為了防治台灣的熱帶傳染病，高等商業學校是為了培養在台灣、華南、南洋從商的專業人才，高等工業學校則設置電氣、應用化學、機械等科，為培養工業發展所需人才。雖然一九二二年承認所謂台、日「共學」，即消除隔離教育政策，但卻設有各種限制，名額也有限，有辦法的家庭都將小孩送

到日本讀書。

　　第三個時期從一九三〇年中期開始，總督府加強普及日語，灌輸日本國民精神等思想。一九三七年中日戰爭爆發後，更積極的推行皇民化教育。

　　總結來說，日本時代台灣教育特色是：

　　一、教育制度始終保留台、日不同的差別待遇。

　　二、教育目的是為實行「皇民化」，企圖將台灣人同化於日本社會，但也激發台灣人的不滿和自覺。

　　三、以初等教育為重心，日治後期公學校快速成長（一九四〇年公學校有八百二十五所，就學率也到了五十二％），有助於日語的普及，也有助於現代基本知識的傳播。

　　四、初等教育重視公民訓練、體育和衛生，教師富敬業精神；中等教育注意職業訓練；高等教育則重視應用科學和學術研究，是值得肯定的。

第 **6** 章
日本人深入山地

The Japanese Exploit
the Mountains

日本人經營台灣殖民地，主要的目的在於獲得經濟利益。台灣山區有樟腦、林木、礦產等，對日本人來說，這些都是不可放過的財富。

The principal reason Japan operated a colony on Taiwan was to reap economic benefits. Taiwan's mountain areas contain camphor, timber, and mineral deposits. These were riches that the Japanese could not overlook.

不過由於山區居住著原住民，對要出入山區、開採山地資源的人來說，構成很大的威脅。

However, indigenous peoples who inhabited the mountain areas posed a considerable threat to the Japanese.

註：本書人物對話部分，為符合故事所設定情境，「原住民」一詞將適時改稱「番人」或「番仔」。
NOTE: To reflect the usage of the times, the term "savages" has been used in place of the contemporary term, "indigenous peoples."

可是山裡有樟腦等寶藏，我們深入山區還是會遇上他們啊！

The mountain areas contain treasures such as camphor. We should enter those areas and face down the indigenous peoples!

何況他們還有獵人頭的習慣，這會造成我方很大的傷害。

But these savages are headhunters and could present a real menace to our people!

我想番人之所以會獵取平地人的人頭，是因為平地人常常欺負他們。我們和西洋人一樣，都是他們的好朋友，應該不會發生這種事。

I think the savages hunted the heads of Chinese settlers because the settlers often mistreated them. We Japanese, like the Westerners, are good friends of the savages.

真的是這樣嗎？

Is that so?

其實番人本性不惡，是可以接受教化的。以後不妨多多召集部落的頭目們，並送些日常用品，就可以趁機教導他們一些禮教了。

The savages are not actually bad by nature. They can be educated. In the future, we can teach them some propriety by calling together a number of village chiefs and giving them some daily necessities.

總督府專心於應付平地
地區的反抗，無暇他顧
，可是那些積極要進入
山地，尤其製造樟腦的
業者並不是很放心。

While the Governor's Office
focused on dealing with
resistance on the plains, they
had no time to deal with other
things. But those who were
eager to exploit the mountain
areas, particularly camphor
traders, were uneasy.

為了保障生命，維護自身
利益，有些業者甚至自行
召募警備人員。

To protect their lives and interests,
some businesses even recruited
armed guards.

直到平地的武裝反抗獲得控制後，總督府才有餘力整頓山地。一九〇六年之後，改變原來的懷柔方針，採取積極的武力征服。

After the armed resistance on the plains was brought under control, the Governor's Office began to deal with the mountain areas. After 1906, Japanese policy shifted from one of conciliation to one of conquest.

日本殖民政府展開所謂的「五年理番事業」。主要重點有三：一、挺進隘勇線。二、征伐原住民。三、扣押原住民槍枝。總督府認為這三者必須同時兼顧，缺一不可。

The Japanese Government implemented its "Five-Year Project to Manage the Savages." This project had three main objectives: 1) advancing the front lines; 2) conquering the indigenous peoples; and 3) disarming the indigenous peoples. The Governor's Office believed that achieving each of these objectives was imperative.

台灣總督府內──
Taiwan Governor's Office

過去清帝國也曾以武力
開山撫番，但是這些部
落仍然叛服無常，根本
的問題在於他們擁有槍
枝。

The Cing Empire once tried to
use military force to "open up
the mountain areas and pacify
the savages," but some tribes
continued to resist. The root
of the problem is that they
have guns.

這個問題已經研究過了，只要以武力直搗
番社，收繳槍械子彈，讓他們無法反抗就
能解決問題。

We have studied the problem. If we use military force to
attack directly the Savage Villages and confiscate their
guns and ammunition, they will be unable to resist.

現在台灣總共有六百八十二個番社
，我們計畫從明年開始，花五年的
時間陸續征討，從北到南、從西到
東，全面控制整個台灣島。

There currently are 682 such villages on
Taiwan. Our plan is to bring them all under
control from north to south and west to east
within five years from next year.

總督府計畫深入山地，向沒有隘勇線的地區推進。推進的方法是先派探險隊勘查地形，劃定路線。只要劃定新的隘勇線，就從四面八方包圍，直接攻擊部落。

The Governor's Office planned to penetrate far into the mountain areas and advance in areas beyond existing frontiers. To accomplish this, reconnaissance teams would be sent to observe the terrain and plot routes. Once new routes had been plotted, the indigenous villages could be easily surrounded for direct assault.

碰！
Crack!

啊！我中槍了！
Ah! I'm hit!

快快！快找掩護！
Quickly! Take cover!

可惡！要你們好看！
Curses! You'll get yours!

為了推進隘勇線，日本
運用優勢的武力，不斷
討伐反抗的原住民。

To advance the frontiers,
Japanese forces used their
superior firepower to
mercilessly punish indigenous
resistance fighters.

開砲！
Fire!

轟！
Boom!

轟！
Boom!

轟！
Boom!

總督府還建了許多的隘
寮堡壘，甚至在隘勇線
上架起鐵絲網，有的還
通上了電。

The Governor's Office also
built numerous fortresses and
even erected barbed wire
fences along the frontiers.
Some of these fences were
even electrified.

隘勇線推進的同時，日本人也積極的在山區開路，並進行林野調查。

While advancing the frontiers, the Japanese aggressively cut roads into mountain areas and began to survey the countryside.

就這樣，隘勇線一層層往山區推進。日本人能控制的山區也就越來越多。

The frontiers were gradually advanced into mountain areas, and the Japanese-controlled area gradually grew.

從一九一〇年到一九一五年
之間，總督府在台灣全島十
二個地域展開作戰。

During the five years from 1910 to
1915, the Governor's Office waged
battles in 12 regions in Taiwan.

原住民大致被鎮壓住了，但總
督府也付出極大的代價，死傷
慘重。

The indigenous peoples were largely
subdued but the Governor's Office had
also paid dearly in military casualties.

原住民被沒收了大
約兩萬枝槍，自此
抵抗力大弱。

During the campaigns,
about 20,000 guns were
confiscated from the
indigenous peoples.
Henceforth, their ability
to resist would be
substantially weakened.

總督府對山地與平地採取隔離統治政策。

The Japanese adopted a policy of separate governance with respect to the plains and mountain areas.

一般人想要入山要有「許可證」，而原住民想離開山地，也要警方的許可。日本人聲稱是要保護原住民，其實是為了避免平地人走私槍枝上山，以方便掌控。

Anyone entering or leaving the mountains needed a police permit. The Japanese claimed to be protecting the indigenous peoples, but the truth was that it prevented Chinese settlers in the plains from smuggling guns into the mountains.

你的證件有問題，不能離開。

You can't leave. There's a problem with your permit.

隨著武力的推進，總督府漸漸掌握住山區的狀況。林野調查、開山通道，也使得山地資源更容易開採、開發。

As their troops advanced, the Governor's Office gradually gained overall control of the mountain areas. The countryside surveys and transportation routes for development of the mountain areas allowed the resources there to be easily extracted and developed.

此時日本人在各個部落中設「警察官駐在所」，直接管理原住民。

Japanese police stations were established in each village to directly rule the indigenous peoples.

駐在所的警察，除了負責維護治安外，還負責其他工作，包括生活指導⋯⋯

In addition to maintaining order, the police stations had other duties. These included providing guidance about daily living.

你們如果和別族的人發生爭吵，一定要向我報告，不可以直接找對方尋仇。

If any dispute should arise between your people and those of other tribes, you must report it directly to me. You can't approach them directly to exact revenge.

農耕指導……
And guidance on farming ...

醫療指導……
... medical care...

還有教育兒童。
... even guidance about parenting.

在山區，日本警察
什麼都要管，簡直
成了土霸王。

In the mountain areas, the police controlled everything. They were de facto feudal lords.

日本人高壓統治原住民，讓原本自由慣了的原住民無法適應。再加上日本人時常壓榨原住民的勞力……

The Japanese governed the indigenous peoples through oppression. The indigenous peoples, used to being free, found it hard to adapt. The Japanese also often subjected them to forced labor.

有時還會欺騙原住民。

Sometimes they would also cheat the indigenous peoples.

大人，為什麼今天不給工資？

Sir, why aren't we being paid today?

沒有就是沒有，幹麼問那麼多！

Not today means not today. Don't ask so many questions.

有些日本人甚至會騙取原住民女子的感情。

Some of the Japanese would even toy with the emotions of indigenous women.

可惡，都娶了人家，居然還敢始亂終棄。

Dastardly! How could he marry you and then abandon you?

嗚……哥哥。

Ooh ... brother.

由於日本警察仗著優勢的武力，在山區作威作福，原住民心中的積怨越來越多。

Their superior firepower enabled the Japanese police to run roughshod over the indigenous peoples, provoking enormous enmity.

到了一九二〇年代，日本人認為已經掌控山地了，便放鬆警戒，開始積極進入山區。

By the 1920s, the Japanese believed that they were in full control of the mountain areas so they loosened their grip and began to actively enter mountain areas.

沒想到卻在一九三〇年，發生了原住民抗暴的「霧社事件」。在這次事件中，原住民把長久積壓在心中的不滿，全部發洩出來。殺戮之慘烈，震驚全台及日本國內。

They hadn't anticipated the 1930 indigenous rebellion known as the Wushe Incident. The indigenous peoples vented long pent-up rage. The ferocity of the slaughter shocked both Taiwan and Japan.

在這次事件中，共有一百三十四個日本人被殺，二百一十五個人受傷。事後，日本做了深入的檢討。

A total of 134 Japanese were killed and 215 people injured.
Japan subsequently conducted a thorough evaluation of the incident.

我認為是少數番人逞勇好鬥所造成的。

I think the rebels are the minority.

我倒不認為完全是這原因。看樣子是我們的政策錯了，警察與番人接觸時態度上有過失，應該也是原因之一。

I don't think so. It seems to be a policy error. Another cause may be that some of our police officers adopt an inappropriate attitude when interacting with the savages.

是啊！要不然番人也不會引起這麼大的暴動，而且只針對日本人而來，平地人反而沒有受害。

Sure! Otherwise the savages would not have become so violent. Also, their violence was not directed at Chinese settlers but only at Japanese.

165

日本人有計畫的將原住民集體遷往靠近平原的山腳地帶。

The Japanese planned to resettle the indigenous peoples in the foothills near the plains.

為什麼要搬到山下？山下又沒有獵物讓我們狩獵。

Why are we moving to the foothills? There's nothing for us to hunt there.

我們祖先以前就住在這裡，不可以說搬就搬。

Our ancestors lived here. We can't just move like that.

不搬！
We're staying!

不搬！
We're staying!

不搬！
We're staying!

原住民一直頑強抵抗日本人的遷移政策，台東還曾發生布農族人襲擊日本人的事件。

The indigenous peoples staunchly resisted Japan's resettlement policy and there was one incident in Taitung where members of the Bunun tribe attacked the Japanese.

可惡的日本人，為什麼要強迫我們搬家？

Confounded Japanese! Why are they forcing us to move?

殺啊！

Kill them!

日本人除了運用優勢的武力脅迫之外，還利用原住民出身的基層警官來勸誘頭目。

To handle such incidents, the Japanese not only utilized their military advantage, but also forced indigenous policemen to persuade tribal leaders.

從一九三〇年開始，到一九四一年為止，遷移的原住民人數共達四萬三千多人。

Between 1930 and 1941, a total of 43,000 indigenous peoples were resettled.

原住民遷移之後，日本人便命令他們在駐在所附近集中居住。

After moving, the Japanese ordered them to cluster their dwellings around local police stations.

你們以後就在駐在所附近定居好了。

In the future, all of you will live near the police station.

看到沒有，日本人最大的目的就是要隨時監視我們。

You see? The Japanese resettled us so that they can constantly monitor us.

咦，你怎麼知道？

Really! How do you know?

別笨了，駐在所就在旁邊，以後我們一舉一動他們都能看得清清楚楚。

Don't be a fool. The police station is right close by. They can easily watch our every move.

將原住民遷移至低海拔地區之後，日本人還對原住民進行「教化」。

After the indigenous peoples were resettled in lower-lying areas, the Japanese began their "education."

其中，重要的目的之一是要讓原住民放棄狩獵，改採農耕生活。

An important part of this was persuading the indigenous peoples to abandon their custom of hunting in favor of cultivation.

大家注意，現在來教你們種水稻。

Pay attention everyone. I am now teaching you how to grow rice.

大人，這麼小的土地，真的能種出很多的稻米嗎？

Sir, can such a small plot really produce a large amount of rice?

學這種耕種方式會不會很困難呢？

Is this going to be hard?

放心，我說過了，我會教你們新的技術。種了水稻，以後就不怕餓肚子，也不必再到山上打獵了。

Don't worry. I told you I would teach you new skills. Once you've learned how to plant rice, you'll have sufficient food supplies, so you won't have to return to the mountains to hunt.

可是打獵是我們的一種習俗，不是吃飽了就可以不打了。

Hunting not only provides us with enough to eat but is also our custom. You can't say that we won't need to hunt anymore simply because we'll have enough to eat.

別管那麼多，現在都已經搬到山下了，還不如好好種田把肚子填飽就好了。

Shut your trap! You've already moved out of the mountains. Shouldn't you be content with planting rice and filling your bellies?

不行呀！
No!

不要那麼固執，把你們的槍都交出來，不要再去打獵了。

Don't be so stubborn. Give up your guns and forgo hunting.

為了能盡快達成同化的目標，日本人在各部族中成立「青年團」，積極培養能接受教化的年輕人。

To accelerate their assimilation policy, the Japanese established "youth brigades" in each tribe. These brigades aggressively cultivated youths who were favorably disposed to being "educated."

他們要能夠說一口流利的日語，用日語吸收新知，並了解同化政策的優點，進而協助積極的推動。日本人最終的目的，是要讓他們能「敬神尊皇」，並且效忠日本國。

They hoped that those indigenous young men would be fluent in Japanese and able to acquire knowledge and understand the advantages of the assimilation policy, and thus help advance that policy. The ultimate objective of the Japanese was to convince the indigenous peoples to "revere the Shinto gods, and honor the Emperor," and to be loyal to Japan.

這些青年團的成員在部落裡發揮了很大的影響力，有的人率先將家裡所藏匿的槍枝交出來。

The members of the Youth Brigades had a major impact within their tribes. Some of them even took their lead in turning in guns that were hidden in their homes.

你瘋了，沒有槍，我們怎麼打獵？

Are you crazy? How can we go hunting with no guns?

這是陋習，這種觀念一定要更正才行。

It's an undesirable custom and must be rectified.

唉，你呀！真不知叫我該說什麼才好。

Ah! I really don't know what to do with you!

有的青年團成員反抗族裡的頭目。

Some members of the Youth Brigades defied their chiefs.

喂！你為什麼不向頭目納貢？

Hey! Why don't you pay tribute to the tribal chief?

為什麼要繳給他？

Why should I pay him?

因為他是頭目啊！

Because he is the chief!

頭目又怎麼樣，這些土地都是天皇陛下的，我絕不會再繳田賦給頭目了。

So what? Huh! All of this land belongs to the Emperor. I'm not paying tribute to the chief anymore.

日本人訓練青年團,希望盡快達成同化的目標,同時瓦解部落的向心力,教化政策才容易施行。

Through training the Youth Brigades, the Japanese hoped the indigenous peoples could be assimilated more swiftly and that the solidarity among the tribes could be broken down. Japan could thus quickly realize its "education" policy.

所以,總督府對青年團全力支持,漸漸的青年團取代了族裡頭目的地位。

So with the full support of the Governor's Office, the Youth Brigades gradually supplanted the roles formerly played by tribal leaders.

日本人想以新世代取代舊世代的目的,也逐漸達成。

As a result, Japan's objective of replacing the old generation with the youth was gradually realized.

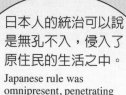

日本人的統治可以說是無孔不入，侵入了原住民的生活之中。

Japanese rule was omnipresent, penetrating every aspect of indigenous peoples' lives.

這是原住民文化的浩劫。

This was a great tragedy for the indigenous peoples.

現在的年輕人，都忘記我們舊有的傳統了。

Our youth have forgotten our age-old customs.

唉！對啊！

Alas! Such a terrible shame!

令人難過的是，許多效忠日本的原住民青年，就這樣將寶貴的生命奉獻出去了。

Even more heart wrenching is that many among the indigenous youth that were loyal to Japan paid for their loyalty with their precious lives.

許多受日本教化的原住民，後來還被日本殖民政府動員到戰場上去作戰。

The Colonial Government later sent to war many of those indigenous peoples "educated" by the Japanese.

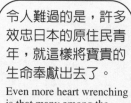

霧社事件

日本警察經常欺壓原住民，強迫他們搬運木材以供建設機關房舍，卻又常藉故不發工錢；而且日本警察一向不尊重原住民的文化，並經常欺負他們的婦女，使得南投霧社賽德克族的原住民忍無可忍，終於起而反抗，這就是發生於一九三〇年十月二十七日的「霧社事件」。

十月七日在馬赫坡社的一場婚禮上，日本警察打了頭目的兒子而遭圍毆，警察揚言將處罰整個部落。部落的青年抱著必死的決心，計畫反抗行動。

十月二十四日開始聯絡與結盟的動作，集結了六社約四百名壯丁。二十六日的夜裡，首先襲擊附近的派出所，奪取彈藥，切斷對外聯絡，最後於二十七日早上趁霧社公學校聯合運動會，發動攻勢，共殺了一百三十四名日本人。

原是日本人引以為傲的霧社模範區，如今卻發生殺戮事件，這震驚了日本朝野。台灣總督調派一千多名警察及八百名軍隊攻山，與原住民對峙長達一個多月。日本飛機從空中丟下傳單並施放毒氣瓦斯，軍隊也殺了許多老弱婦孺，最後馬赫坡社頭目莫那魯道與起事青年自殺，六社原有一千四百多名原住民，卻只剩五百名，而且被強制遷移。

一九三一年四月二十五日，日本又提供武器給敵對的「味方番」，霧社原住民又被屠殺二百一十人，剩餘二百八十九人被遷移到川中島社，這是所謂的「第二次霧社事件」。

《認識台灣歷史》第七、八冊共用此份年表

年代		台灣大事記
一八九五年	光緒二十一年 日本明治二十八年	◎四月十七日：馬關條約中承認朝鮮國獨立，大清帝國割讓台灣、遼東給日本。 ◎五月二十五日：唐景崧、丘逢甲等人成立「台灣民主國」。 ◎五月二十九日：日軍登陸澳底鹽寮（位於現今的台北縣貢寮鄉）。 ◎六月四日：唐景崧內渡回中國。台灣人持續抵抗日軍長達五個月。 ◎十月十九日：劉永福逃離台灣，「台灣民主國」亡。
一八九六年	明治二十九年	◎三月三十日：日本政府公布「六三法」。
一八九九年	明治三十二年	◎日本殖民政府依「匪徒刑罰令」，處死一〇二三人。 ◎開始修築從基隆到高雄的縱貫鐵路。 ◎台灣銀行開始營業。 ◎台北師範開校。 ◎台北自來水、排水溝系統完成。
一九〇〇年	明治三十三年	◎台北、台南開始設立公用電話。
一九〇一年	明治三十四年	◎台灣總督府公布「總督府專賣局官制」，樟腦、鴉片、食鹽為專賣品，並設於同一局內。
一九〇三年	明治三十六年	◎第一個水力發電所在桃園龜山成立。 ◎成立「臨時台灣番地調查事務委員會」。

年代		台灣大事記
一九〇五年	明治三十八年	◎十月一日：第一次戶口普查。
一九〇六年	明治三十九年	◎統一度量衡。
一九〇七年	明治四十年	◎四月二十七日：「北埔事件」爆發。
一九〇八年	明治四十一年	◎二月二十九日：公布「官設埤圳規則」。 ◎四月二十日：縱貫鐵路全線通車。 ◎高雄港正式開工築港（一九〇八年至一九一二年）。
一九〇九年	明治四十二年	◎埔里社支廳泰雅族二十六社反抗。
一九一〇年	明治四十三年	◎五年理番計畫開始。
一九一一年	明治四十四年	◎統一台灣貨幣。 ◎阿里山鐵路全線通車。 ◎十月二十六日：任用本地人為巡查（基層警員）。
一九一四年	大正三年	◎第一次世界大戰爆發（一九一四年至一九一八年）。 ◎鎮壓太魯閣原住民。
一九一五年	大正四年	◎余清芳以神明指示為由，號召西來庵信徒反抗日軍，日軍屠殺近千人。 ◎台灣總督府開發八仙山、宜蘭太平山森林。
一九一九年	大正八年	◎台北市公共汽車開始營業。
一九二一年	大正十年	◎一月十七日：「台灣文化協會」成立。 ◎「台灣議會設置請願運動」開始。

年代		台灣大事記
一九二三年	大正十二年	◎黃呈聰發表〈論普及白話文的新使命〉，黃朝琴發表〈漢文改革論〉，蔡培火發表〈台灣新文學運動與羅馬字〉。首創台灣白話運動先河。
一九二四年	大正十三年	◎七星畫壇成立（倪蔣懷、陳澄波、陳英聲、陳承藩、藍蔭鼎、陳植棋、陳銀用）。
一九二五年	大正十四年	◎十月二十二日：爆發「二林事件」，蔗農為爭取權益與警察發生衝突。
一九二六年	昭和元年	◎三月二十七日：台東到花蓮鐵路線開通。 ◎六月二十八日：「台灣農民組合」成立。
一九二九年	昭和四年	◎糾紛二十多年的「竹林事件」，被迫解決；日本殖民政府要求各庄出錢購回竹林，繼續抗爭的農民則以警力鎮壓。
一九三○年	昭和五年	◎四月十日：嘉南大圳通水起用。 ◎九月二十二日：農民包圍學甲、下營、佳里、麻豆各地庄役所，要求減免水租。 ◎十月二十七日：發生「霧社事件」。
一九三四年	昭和九年	◎五月十一日：日本四大財閥決定合辦台鋁公司。
一九三五年	昭和十年	◎十一月二十二日：舉行台灣首次投票，選舉地方議員。
一九三六年	昭和十一年	◎三月三十日：松山機場竣工。
一九三七年	昭和十二年	◎六月一日：台灣船塢公司成立。 ◎七月七日：中日戰爭爆發，日本改派軍人為台灣總督。 ◎七月三十一日：日月潭第二期發電所竣工。
一九四○年	昭和十五年	◎推行改用日本姓名運動。

年代		台灣大事記
一九四一年	昭和十六年	◎二月八日：台灣總督府公布禁止台灣人使用舊曆（陰曆）。 ◎四月十九日：「皇民奉公會」成立。 ◎十二月八日：日本轟炸美國的太平洋基地，開啟美日戰爭。
一九四二年	昭和十七年	◎日軍募集台灣人為「陸軍志願兵」。
一九四三年	昭和十八年	◎強迫農民交出白米，實施糧食管制與配給。 ◎強徵台、韓籍學生赴前線。
一九四五年	昭和二十年	◎美軍飛機轟炸台灣各地。 ◎八月十五日：日本無條件投降，也結束日本在台五十一年的統治。

發現台灣，考考你！

看漫畫書好玩吧，你對台灣的歷史有更多的認識了嗎？下面的題目可以讓你和父母、老師、朋友們討論，分享彼此的想法。一起走進歷史，發現台灣吧！

1 甲午戰爭以後，
日本和清帝國簽下什麼條約，割讓台灣和澎湖？

2 台灣剛割讓給日本的時候，
曾出現「台灣民主國」，你知道它成立的原因嗎？

3 台灣割讓給日本之後，
日本政府是否將台灣人視為日本人對待？

4 土豪在清代是台灣社會自治的一股重要力量，
到了台灣統治時卻不是，這是為什麼？

5 日本為了從台灣獲得經濟利益，做了許多基礎建設，
你能舉出一些例子來嗎？

6 日本為了改善台灣的醫療環境而蓋台北醫院，
它是今日的哪一家醫院？

7 日本在台灣設立學校，鼓勵台灣人上學，
這種學校與以前孔廟附設的學校有什麼不同？

8 台灣現今許多制度是日本時代遺留下來的，
你能舉出三個例子嗎？

9 日本人為了開採山區資源，進行「理番」政策，
這與清帝國的「開山撫番」相比，
你覺得哪一種政策對原住民的迫害比較深？

10 「霧社事件」之後，
日本對原住民的政策有了什麼樣的轉變？

製作群介紹

◎總策劃
吳密察
現職：台灣大學歷史系副教授
學歷：日本東京大學博士課程修了，專攻台灣史、日本近代史

◎漫畫繪製
劉素珍
現職：[102視覺概念工作室] 負責人
學歷：日本東京設計家學院室內設計科畢業

◎漫畫繪製
劉昭淵
現職：任職於[102視覺概念工作室]
學歷：景文技術學院視覺傳達系

◎劇本編寫
鄭丞鈞
現職：國小教師
學歷：台東大學兒童文學研究所碩士

◎附錄資料撰寫
陳雅文
現職：編輯
學歷：台灣大學歷史系畢業

◎英文版策劃
文魯彬（Robin J. Winkler）
現職：台灣蠻野心足生態協會理事長、博仲法律事務所（本國與外國法事務律師事務所）合夥律師。1977年旅居台灣，於2003年放棄美國籍後，歸化為中華民國國籍。

◎英文審訂
翁佳音
現職：中央研究院台灣史研究所助研究員
學歷：台灣大學歷史研究所碩士，曾留學荷蘭萊頓大學（Leiden）攻讀歐洲擴張史；專攻十七、八世紀台灣史

◎英文審訂
賴慈芸
現職：台灣師範大學翻譯研究所助理教授
學歷：香港理工大學中文及雙語研究系博士

◎英文審訂
耿柏瑞（Brian A. Kennedy）
現職：博仲法律事務所（本國與外國法事務律師事務所）編譯員
學歷：美國馬里蘭大學新聞學及東亞學雙學位

◎英文翻譯
何仁傑（Peter Hillman）
現職：專業中英口譯員
學歷：美國華盛頓州立大學企業管理學士

Editorial Staff

◎ Editor-in-Chief
Wu Mi-cha

Wu Mi-cha is an associate professor with National Taiwan University's Department of History.
He received an M.A. degree from the University of Tokyo's Graduate School of Arts and Sciences, specializing in Taiwan history and the history of modern Japan.

◎ Cartoon Illustration
Kate Liu

Kate Liu is the owner of 102 Image Concept Studio. She graduated from the Tokyo College of Design.

◎ Cartoon Illustrator
Kane Liu

Kane Liu is an employee of 102 Image Concept Studios. He is a student at Jin Wen Institute of Technology's School of Visual Communication Design.

◎ Cartoon Script
Jheng Cheng-chun

Jheng Cheng-chun is a primary school teacher. He received an M.A. degree from National Taitung University's Graduate Institute of Children's Literature.

◎ Editorial Researcher
Grace Chen

Grace Chen works as a newspaper editor. She holds a B.A. degree in history from National Taiwan University.

◎ Chief English Editor
Robin J. Winkler

Robin J. Winkler is director of the Taiwan Wild at Heart Legal Defense Association and founding partner of Winkler Partners, Attorneys of Domestic and Foreign Legal Affairs. Having come to Taiwan in 1977, he gave up his U.S. citizenship to become a naturalized citizen of Taiwan in 2003.

◎ English Editor
Ang Kaim

Ang Kaim is a research fellow at Academia Sinica's Institute of Taiwan History. He received an M.A. degree in history from National Taiwan University.
He studied the History of European Expansion at Leiden University in the Netherlands, specializing in the history of Taiwan during the 17th and 18th centuries.

◎ English Editor
Sharon Lai

Sharon Lai is assistant professor at the Graduate Institute of Translation and Interpretation, National Taiwan Normal University. She received her Ph.D. in Chinese and bilingual studies from Hong Kong Polytechnic University.

◎ Series Editor
Brian A. Kennedy

Brian A. Kennedy is a legal translator for Winkler Partners. He holds a combined B.A. degree in journalism and East Asian studies from the University of Maryland.

◎ English Translator
Peter Hillman

Peter Hillman is a freelance Chinese-English interpreter. He received a B.A. degree in business administration from the University of Washington.

認識台灣歷史

A HISTORY OF TAIWAN IN COMICS

原《漫畫台灣史》增訂
All new edition

● 總策劃〉吳密察　Editor-in-Chief: Wu Mi-cha
● 英文版策劃〉文魯彬　Chief English Editor: Robin J. Winkler

知識漫畫版・中英對照・全部彩圖演出
Educational comics · Bilingual Chinese-English format · Full-color illustrations

第一部精采・有趣・可雙語學習的台灣史

A fascinating and compelling bilingual history of Taiwan

配合教學互動的五大貼心設計

[話說台灣歷史]●每冊附台大歷史系吳密察教授的精心導讀,輕鬆掌握全書重點與全貌。

[看漫畫學歷史]●漫畫活潑生動、中英雙語演出,帶領大家從歷史中得到樂趣,從樂趣中了解歷史。

[台灣歷史小百科]●60則史實與趣聞兼顧的歷史小百科,增加台灣歷史常識。

[台灣歷史年表]●每冊附台灣歷史大事年表,方便教學和複習。

[台灣歷史常識問答]●100題激發思考的台灣歷史問答題,方便老師出題、同學相互問答,增加親子話題。

 新自然主義股份有限公司
THIRD NATURE PUBLISHING CO., LTD.

Purchasing Information:
http：// www.thirdnature.com.tw

建議以下對象必讀
Recommended as a "must-read" for the following:

1 **國小中高年級、中學生**
Older primary and middle school students
認識台灣歷史、增進英文的最佳課外讀物

2 **中小學教師**
Primary and middle school teachers
教學上最佳輔助本土教材、英文教材

3 **學校圖書館**
School libraries
借閱率最高的必備好書

4 **外國友人**
Foreign friends
輕鬆認識台灣的第一本書

5 **所有新台灣人**
Every "New Taiwanese"
了解台灣歷史必讀入門書、人人都可以用
英文為外國人介紹台灣

了解台灣，從《認識台灣歷史》開始 A greater understanding of Taiwan starts with "A History of Taiwan in Comics"

1 **遠古時代：南島語族的天地**
Ancient Times: Austronesian Origins

2 **荷蘭時代：冒險者的樂園**
The Dutch Era: A Paradise for European Adventurers

3 **鄭家時代：鄭氏集團的興衰**
The Koxinga Period: The Rise and Fall of the Jheng Regime

4 **清朝時代（上）：唐山過台灣**
The Cing Dynasty (I): Leaving the Mainland for Taiwan

5 **清朝時代（中）：羅漢腳的世界**
The Cing Dynasty (II): The World of the "Wandering Bachelors"

6 **清朝時代（下）：戰爭陰影下的建設**
The Cing Dynasty (III): Construction Under the Shadow of War

7 **日本時代（上）：日本資本家的天堂**
The Japanese Era (I): The Backyard of Japan's Capitalists

8 **日本時代（下）：覺醒的年代**
The Japanese Era (II): The Age of Awakening

9 **戰後（上）：強人天空下**
The Post-World War II Era (I): In the Realm of the Strongmen

10 **戰後（下）：改革與開放**
The Post-World War II Era (II): Reform and Openness

○○○ **全套買省更多** ○○○

典藏版10冊＋電子書1片／全套3500元
普及版10冊／全套2500元／全套買省更多，歡迎來電洽詢最新優惠方案。

Save even more on a complete set :
Hardcover 10-volume edition + CD-Rom: NT$3500; Paperback 10-volume edition: NT$2500.
Call for details on the latest promotions.

訂購專線：**886-2-27845369**
Call to order: 886-2-27845369

劃撥帳號：**17239354**／新自然主義股份有限公司
Purchasing Information: http://www.thirdnature.com.tw

國家圖書館出版品預行編目資料

認識台灣歷史.7，日本時代（上）：日本資本家的天堂
=A History of Taiwan in Comics.7,
　The Japanese Era (I): The Backyard of
　Japan's Capitalists/ 鄭丞鈞劇本編寫 ；劉素珍、
劉昭淵漫畫繪製；何仁傑（Peter Hillman）英譯.
--初版. --臺北市：新自然主義. 2005〔民94〕
　　面：　　公分
中英對照
ISBN 957-696-590-X（精裝）
ISBN 957-696-568-3（平裝）
1. 臺灣 - 歷史 - 漫畫與卡通

673.22　　　　　　　　　　　　　　93016518

認識台灣歷史 ❼

原《漫畫台灣史》增訂

A HISTORY OF TAIWAN IN COMICS

日本時代（上）：日本資本家的天堂
The Japanese Era (I): The Backyard of Japan's Capitalists

總策劃：吳密察
漫畫繪製：[102工作室] 劉素珍、劉昭淵、林柏輝
劇本編寫：鄭丞鈞 / 資料編寫：陳雅文
英文版策劃：文魯彬（Robin J. Winkler）
英文審訂：翁佳音、賴慈芸、耿柏瑞（Brian A. Kennedy）
英文翻譯：何仁傑（Peter Hillman）

初版：2005年3月
一版六刷：2008年6月
典藏版定價：新台幣350元
普及版定價：新台幣250元
郵撥帳號：17239354　新自然主義股份有限公司
地址：台北市建國南路二段9號10樓之2
電話：886-2-27845369
傳真：886-2-27845358
網址：www.thirdnature.com.tw
E-mail：moonsun@ms18.hinet.net

版權所有・翻印必究 Printed in Taiwan
本書如有缺頁、破損、倒裝，請寄回更換。
ISBN 957-696-590-X（精裝）
ISBN 957-696-568-3（平裝）

出版者：新自然主義股份有限公司
發行人：洪美華
總編輯：蔡幼華
專案統籌：黃信瑜
編譯協力：王興安、吳恬綺、葛窈君、關山行（K. Mark. Brown）
版型設計：唐亞陽工作室
美術設計：陳巧玲
編輯部：劉又甄、何靜茹、高美鈴
市場部：張惠卿、劉秀芬、洪秋蓉、黃麗珍
管理部：洪美月、巫毓麗、陳候光、鄭欽祐

製版：凱立國際資訊股份有限公司
印刷：久裕印刷事業股份有限公司

總經銷：農學股份有限公司
台北縣新店市寶橋路235巷6弄6號2樓
電話：886-2-29178022　傳真：886-2-29156275

Call to Order: 886-2-27845369
Website: www.thirdnature.com.tw

特別感謝「博仲法律事務所」（本國與外國法事務律師事務所）的協助。

一部最精采有趣、具學術基礎、完整又翔實的台灣史
適合9到99歲的大人小孩閱讀

知識漫畫版《認識台灣歷史》（全套10冊），

不但中英對照，而且全部彩圖演出，

編繪遠古、荷西、鄭氏時代、清代、日本時代以及戰後六個時期，

重新勾勒台灣史脈絡與全貌，

更反映各階段台灣人的生活方式與價值觀，

了解台灣，就從這部《認識台灣歷史》開始。

（請沿線對摺，免貼郵票寄回本公司）

姓名：　　　　　　電話：（　　）

地址：

新自然主義股份有限公司
THIRD NATURE PUBLISHING CO., LTD.
地址：106 台北市建國南路二段9號10樓之2

Call to Order：886-2-27845369 FAX：886-2-27845358

E-mail：book@thirdnature.com.tw

劃撥帳號：17239354 新自然主義股份有限公司

Website：www.thirdnature.com.tw

新自然主義 讀者回函卡

謝謝您購買本書,為加強對讀者的服務並使往後的出書更臻完善,請您詳填本卡各欄,傳真(886-2-27845358)或投入郵筒寄回(免貼郵票),我們將隨時為您提供最新的出版訊息,以及活動相關資料。

書籍名稱:【認識台灣歷史】第_____冊

購買本書的方式:

☐01在_____市(縣)_____書局購買 ☐02劃撥 ☐03贈送
☐04展覽、演講活動,名稱_____ ☐05其他_____

您從何處得知本書消息?

☐01逛書店 ☐02報紙廣告 ☐03報紙、雜誌介紹 ☐04親友推薦 ☐05書訊
☐06廣播節目 ☐07其他_____

您對我們的建議:_____
_____

您的個人資料:姓名_____ 電子信箱:_____
性　　別:☐男 ☐女 **出生日期:**_____年_____月_____日
電　　話:(　)_____ **傳　　真:**(　)_____
地　　址:☐☐☐_____縣(市)_____鄉鎮區(市)_____路(街)
_____段____巷____弄____號____樓

教育程度:☐01小學 ☐02國中 ☐03高中(職) ☐04大專 ☐05碩士 ☐06博士
職　　業:☐01學生 ☐02教育 ☐03軍警 ☐04其他公務 ☐05金融業 ☐06出版傳播
☐07醫藥 ☐08資訊科技 ☐09法律工作 ☐10其他自由業 ☐11其他服務業
☐12製造業 ☐13家管 ☐14其他_____

閱讀嗜好:☐身心靈健康 ☐醫學保健 ☐本土文化 ☐漫畫 ☐原住民 ☐環保生態 ☐有機生活
☐學習成長 ☐財經商業 ☐生活百科 ☐人物傳記 ☐政治 ☐法律 ☐歷史 ☐宗教

您最常收聽的廣播節目:_____
_____

您最常閱讀的雜誌或報紙:_____
_____